A N

AMERICAN TALE

OF

Crime & Courage,

Betrayal & Heroism, and

FREEDOM'S PROMISE

A gripping and unique story, splendidly illustrated,
that imparts knowledge of the critical years
of our nation's founding struggle...

Patrick Michael McFadden

LIBERTAS ⸸ AMERICANA

An American Tale of Freedom's Promise

by Patrick Michael McFadden

PUBLISHER

Libertas Americana, LLC

WEBSITE

Libertas-Americana.com

BOOK DESIGN

Nancy Starkman
nstar@StarPrintBrokers.com

PRINTING

Star Print Brokers
Bellevue, Washington
StarPrintBrokers.com

ISBN

978-0-578-82520-5

First printing

Bulk and corporate sales may be available. Scholastic discounts may also be available. Contact the pubisher at sales@Libertas-Americana.com.

This book is printed on acid-free paper.

DEDICATION

Dedicated to all who serve.

TABLE OF CONTENTS

LIST OF ILLUSTRATIONS

INTRODUCTION

COMMENTS ON THE BOOK'S ILLUSTRATIONS are enlightening and should be read in line with the story. The commentary can be found with the acknowledgements and notes in the back of the book. A map detailing the entire region covered by the story is located at the end of Chapter One. Created in 1777 and updated for the reader, the map will provide the reader with some bearings throughout the story. Again, comments on the map will be found with the notes.

Our story will hopefully enlighten readers with a chronology that covers the first three years of the armed conflict we know as the Revolutionary War, our founding liberation from an old tyranny. The unlikely antagonists that wind through our story are young Quaker brothers, their brash cousin and a band of "marooned" Indian braves left behind in eastern Pennsylvania as most of their kin have long departed for the Ohio country. The Doan cousins, Moses and Abraham, cultivate an image of invincibility. Before their criminal exploits are known, the pair is widely revered and feared as two of the most dominate athletes and skilled backwoodsman of the Mid-Atlantic colonies.

Pennsylvania is full of patriots at the outbreak of war with Great Britain, yet it is also home to many self-sufficient landowners, especially among the Quakers of Bucks County, whose aversion to military conflict and wealth prevent their enthusiasm for the revolutionary cause. The early war is very much a civil war, as the thirteen colonies possess many loyalists with strong residual support for the English crown.

The Doan brothers and their cousin are no ordinary Quakers, and they respond to the taxation placed on their family lands by the new provisional government in Philadelphia with a decade long crime spree that would make the nineteenth century James gang blush with envy. Surely, many Quakers hung their heads as the Doan boys committed armed highway robbery, horse theft, and even murder throughout the Mid-Atlantic region. The Doan gang's long career is testament to their intelligence, audacity, and both the fear and loyalty that many of their neighbors must have felt.

The Battle of Trenton on the morning after Christmas 1776 is a turning point in our story as it is for the nation, and the Doan play a critical role leading up to the battle, as they have been supplying British forces with horses and intelligence for months. Our nation is yet an infant, less than half a year old by that fateful Christmas. The British Empire meant to smother the new nation in the cradle and had all the means to do so. Like Jesus at Bethlehem or Moses in the reed basket, a fledgling United States makes an improbable escape, and in 1777 the nation quickly grows into a fighting adolescent, trading blows with and often defeating tested European armies.

If 1776 is the year we declare our independence and escape a grim fate, 1777 is the year we become a nation by force of arms and stubborn determination. General George Washington embodies the determination of this *1776 & 1777 project*, and if he had been killed or captured many of his squabbling subordinates would likely have given up the young nation for no more than the promise of a peerage.

No one would have been surprised if the American Revolution died in the first hours of the Battle of Brooklyn, and in fact it almost did, yet the battle is largely forgotten by Americans. The frenzied patriotism of New England caught the English off guard in 1775, and they are run out of Boston with losses remembered to this day. In less than half a year, the king's generals return with the largest foreign invasion force in North America's history, including tens of thousands of German and Scottish troops. British officials would request soldiers and other military support from the Russian Empire as well. However, Catherine the Great demurred, believing the American cause to be justified and seeing the new nation as a potential economic partner.

The battle for control of New York City (The Battle of Brooklyn) is the first and largest major engagement of the entire Revolutionary War, a conflict that will drag on for most of a decade. The Declaration of Independence, signed in Philadelphia, is yet a month old when Lord Richard Howe, Admiral of Britain's North American fleet, and his younger brother, General Sir William Howe's forces arrive in New York harbor with an armada so vast a man could nearly walk from Staten Island to Brooklyn. American heroism during the Battle of Brooklyn is worth knowing and begs the question why so few of us know it.

The Continental Army lost nearly every engagement it fought in between Howe's landing and the surprise American attack on German forces early during the morning of December 26 at Trenton, New Jersey. King George III of Great Britain believes George Washington will make himself king of North America if victorious in battle, and George III stubbornly processes the war with a belief that it is a competition for sovereignty between two men. King George holds this belief until Washington relinquishes power and steps down from his presidency, after a second term, just prior to the turn of a new century. Once word reaches the king of Washington's decision, George III may be recounted as stating, "Then he is a better man than I."

King George III is only the current Queen's third great-grandfather. Certainly, Elizabeth II and her council have not forgotten what was lost in 1776. Hopefully, we as Americans won't allow our children to forget what was gained. After a decade of war, peace negotiations in Europe and a Constitutional Convention, an anxious woman waiting outside Independence Hall in Philadelphia asks an elderly Benjamin Franklin whether the nation has been bequeathed a new monarchy or a republic. Franklin responds, "A republic, if you can keep it, Madam."

*Never before in the history of the world
has a sociopolitical document
expressed in such profound,
eloquent and unequivocal language
the dignity and worth
of human personality.*

————————

STATEMENT PERTAINING TO THE
DECLARATION OF INDEPENDENCE
DR. MARTIN LUTHER KING JR., 1965

The unanimous Declaration of the thirteen united States of America, *When in the Course of human events, it becomes necessary for one people to dissolve the political bands which have connected them with another, and to assume among the powers of the earth, the separate and equal station to which the Laws of Nature and of Nature's God entitle them, a decent respect to the opinions of mankind requires that they should declare the causes which impel them to the separation.*

We *hold these truths to be self-evident, that all men are created equal, that they are endowed by their Creator with certain unalienable Rights, that among these are Life, Liberty and the pursuit of Happiness.—That to secure these rights, Governments are instituted among Men, deriving their just powers from the consent of the governed,—That whenever any Form of Government becomes destructive of these ends, it is the Right of the People to alter or to abolish it, and to institute new Government, laying its foundation on such principles and organizing its powers in such form, as to them shall seem most likely to effect their Safety and Happiness. Prudence, indeed, will dictate that Governments long established should not be changed for light and transient causes; and accordingly all experience hath shewn, that mankind are more disposed to suffer, while evils are sufferable, than to right themselves by abolishing the forms to which they are accustomed. But when a long train of abuses and usurpations, pursuing invariably the same Object evinces a design to reduce them under absolute Despotism, it is their right, it is their duty, to throw off such Government, and to provide new Guards for their future security… We, therefore, the Representatives of the united States of America, in General Congress, Assembled, appealing to the Supreme Judge of the world for rectitude of our intentions, do, in the Name, and by Authority of the good People of these Colonies, solemnly publish and declare, That these United Colonies are, and of Right ought to be Free and Independent States; that they are Absolved from all Allegiance to the British Crown…*

RATIFIED VIA CONGRESS ON JULY 4, 1776.

CHAPTER ONE

SCENE 1

Into the Woods

FOUR MEN are running quickly through the deep woods of colonial Pennsylvania. The trailing man catches a flashing glimpse of their chasers. Indian braves, in silhouette from the darkness of the heavily shadowed woods, are closing in from behind. The front-runners are propelled by a deadly anticipation. The terrain becomes steep, sunlight penetrates the thinning forest, and a younger man loses his footing, falling face first. War whoops are heard from behind the leaders, and the fallen man is presumed caught and killed. Seconds later, the leaders bound across a rocky stream, and a second man stumbles and falls. The scene stays with the remaining leaders as their pace quickens, and the runners sprint out of the dark woods into newly planted fields.

From behind, bodies can be heard bursting through underbrush and branches into the open. The second man yells to the leader, "They are coming." The effort on both men's faces is clear. They pull abreast, briefly, and the leader is passed. Yelling is heard, and the new leader's view rises to a cheering crowd holding a blue and white finish banner high. The new leader is now sprinting hard on grass, and he bursts across the finishing line, hands held high, to the cheers of the crowd. There is a sense of mild relief as the winner turns to the second-place finisher, whose hands are on his knees, and exclaims, "Close race, cousin." Colonial men and Indians stream across the finish.

A young muddy-faced runner, Mahlon Doan, approaches smiling and places a hand on the shoulder of the bent over man, exclaiming, "Brother Moses, has Abraham beaten you again?" Brother Aaron approaches and yells to the group, "Let us find Levi before he finds trouble. He's likely boasting and throwing hawks with the Lenape." Abraham, still smiling from the win, turns and accidentally bangs shoulders with a scowling Mohawk warrior, who stands too close and gives no room in a hardened jealousy. Abraham asks the brave whether he's lost, alluding to the race as well as to the man not being on his own tribal land. The brave replies that he hopes to see Abraham on familiar ground in the future, so he may experience "a loss." They trade menacing smiles, but Abraham is in too good a mood and shrugs off the encounter. He and his cousins enter the fair looking for refreshments, celebration and more.

SCENE 2

May Fair and Flaxen Hair

The May Fair • near Quakertown, Pennsylvania • 1776

Typical scenes of commerce and recreation are to be found at the fair, as crowds mingle among wool merchants and food vendors. Various games and competitions are being held, and young men and women look for excuses to engage one another. A young Quaker woman catches the eye of a group of Mohawk and Lenape warriors. She is attractive with light-flowing hair many braves desire, but travels with a female chaperon, possibly an older relative, and some Dutch merchants. Only the Mohawk ambassador is bold enough to approach but is thwarted when Moses Doan introduces himself.

Teasing, the young women's first words are, "You lost, Sir?" Abraham replies for him, "Aye, he is forever lost." Moses speaks up with a smile, "But no loser in life, I hope," which makes the women blush mildly. The young woman replies, "Should you not be more concerned with your liberty than your life presently?" She wonders why the two men have not joined General Washington's army. Moses replies, "God has already granted my liberty, Miss!" She replies, "Then you should be about it, Sir," abruptly dismissing him. Moses asks if they should part without polite introduction and formally introduces Abraham and himself. Before the young Betsy Ross can say more, her aunt speaks up, "This is my niece, Elizabeth," and bids the cousins farewell.

The sulking young Mohawk brave, an Iroquois ambassador to the Lenape Indians of the upper Delaware River, closely watches the Doan gang, including rogue warriors of the Wolf clan, as they celebrate and harass Mahlon and Levi, who both try to out-throw Indians and settlers alike with the tomahawk. Neither Moses nor Abraham shows the need to display a deadly skill, and none but the visiting Mohawk misses the competition. Standing in a group of Indian spectators, the young Mohawk leader turns to an elderly Lenape chieftain, technically his conquered subordinate, and blurts in the Algonquin tongue, "Grandfather, who are those devils?" The Lenape chief calmly replies in English, "Devils or the Doan."

Abraham, although amused by his cousins, turns his attention to a raven-haired woman and her family, who approach him directly. The young Mohawk ambassador takes note of the tender and polite manner Abraham affords the family. Inquiring with a member of the Wolf band, the Mohawk learns family members are prosperous merchants from nearby Aquetong, and that Abraham intends the woman as his fiancé.

SCENE 3

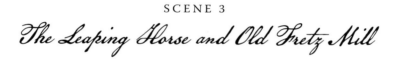

Aquetong Heights • Bucks County, Pennsylvania • evening of May 2, 1776

Abraham, Moses, and an Indian companion, known to the English as Jacob Wolfe, travel on horseback to the home of Peggy Morgan and her father, William. Jacob is an expert tracker, and the small band of braves he leads are descendants of the few Lenni Lenape family groups who remained in northeastern Pennsylvania following the evictions of the 1740s. Moses Doan lived briefly with Jacob's clan, and Jacob treats him as a brother, showing a respect and loyalty sealed by a debt unknown even to Abraham.

Evening approaches and the men make slow progress over the hilly wooded roads. Jacob complains, "You should have named this Penn's Hills," and laughter ensues, but Moses is intent on the path and halts the group abruptly with a hand gesture. He jumps down, with Jacob right behind, and the men realize riders have traveled hurriedly through the sparsely used lane. Jacob turns toward Abraham, with concern on his face, stating, "The Mohawk were asking questions about the Morgans." Abraham violently spurs his steed and is gone before more can be said. Moses and Jacob remount their horses and are chasing before the dust settles. The Morgan home, near the Old Fretz Mill, is not far.

The young Mohawk ambassador, with three warriors and a guide, hides in the wooded slopes across a clearing from the Morgan home. Peggy Morgan and her younger brother, Thomas, are in the front garden, while her father speaks with a mill worker farther down the hill. The Mohawk split-up, aiming to pin down William Morgan and capture Peggy.

Darkness begins to fall as the sun begins to set behind Abraham. Headed east on a downhill slope, his horse is in full cantor and knows the path. A musket shot is heard in the distance, and Abraham hardens the pace. More shots are fired, screams and yelling are heard, and Abraham is barely aware that his cousin is fast on his heals. The Doan break from the wooded lane and go about their bloody work without hesitation. Abraham throws an axe at the gallop, hitting a Mohawk square above the breastplate. Moses kills the Munsee scout with a pistol shot, while Jacob quickly brings up a carbine and shoots the farthest Mohawk. The surviving Mohawk bolts for the woods and makes it to a horse. A deadly chase ensues.

A shot rings out from the porch, and Abraham's horse rears high. The Mohawk ambassador has fired a pistol while gripping Peggy's dress with his free hand. Peggy rips away and falls to the wooded floor as Abraham bounds from his horse, catching the Mohawk's wrist and quickly slicing tendons and muscle under the arm with a large saddle knife. Shots and screams can be heard as Jacob executes a wounded Mohawk brave. Abraham has broken the skull of the young warrior and drags him from the stoop. Jacob can be heard saying, "The ambassador's duties are done," in his native tongue, and encourages Abraham to take a battle prize against his tribal foe. The young Mohawk mumbles what sounds like devil or Doan. Abraham has rage in his eyes and needs no encouragement from Jacob. Staring through Peggy, he scalps the Mohawk in a hard, clean motion while yelling, "My name is Abraham Doan." William Morgan yells out "God, No!" while Peggy screams and Jacob ends the man's suffering with his knife.

Moses chases the surviving Mohawk down a steep, rocky wooded path. He knows the danger ahead, but the Mohawk's horse suddenly stumbles, and Moses' horse leaps the animal, sending both riders and animals over a shale cliff. Moses breaks his fall in a tall Pine, while the Mohawk brave is killed on the ragged ground below. Jacob and William begin a search for Moses, and the two men rescue him with rope once he is found. William asks Jacob to help him dispose of the bodies. He also suggests Abraham and Moses head back north and cross the Delaware River near the old Durham Forge. Abraham protests as he wishes to stay with Peggy. Moses intends to take the horses to the Tory's ferry, at nearby Temple Bar, selling the horses to royalist Tories near Pennington. In disagreement, William Morgan retorts with a stern but sad tone, "Abraham, you bloody marshal man, do what I ask, for these acts will weight heavily on my family were Joseph Brant to hear of them."

Moses and Abraham concede to William's wishes, and they ride north for the Durham Ferry. The cousins reach western Jersey before morning. Moses suggests stealing horses from a large Whig estate in Hunterdon, then transporting the animals north of Princeton. Royal supporters in the region gather supplies for General Howe's coming invasion and will pay in golden guineas. The two men instead ride on for Ringo's Tavern, where their presence will provide some alibi. Leaving prior to dawn, they may more easily abscond with the mounts of borders as well. Both heartily agree on the plan, as stealing horses from known supporters of Washington's army will spread the Doan's notoriety and enhance their alibi for the Mohawk's disappearance.

Both men make advances toward a young tavern maid who works late at the bar. The maid, Hannah Miller, is the daughter of local patriots. Abraham sweet-talks the girl, and she leaves the bar to find room at the Inn for the cousins. On her return, however, Abraham is rebuffed as patrons apprise the woman of the Doan's loyalties. Abraham will remember the slight.

The following morning, Moses inquires with a Princeton blacksmith, whom he has previously used as a fence, about selling a few horses to loyalists. The smith cannot deal directly with local theft, but indicates a wealthy Tory businessman, named Galloway, has fled Philadelphia and is buying up horses and supplies in the region. Moses speaks with Galloway directly, who offers him twenty guineas for the "fine" animals. Galloway, the technical owner of the Durham Furnace, is acquainted with Joseph Doan Sr., knows his son Moses by reputation and is delighted to learn of their distain for and grievance with the Continental Congress in Philadelphia.

Distrustful of the high offer, Moses is put at ease when Galloway predicates payment on the Doan gang rendering him a larger service. They are to visit John Thomlinson's farm in Newtown, Bucks County, retrieve a few dozen horses and packed supplies. No wagons will slow their effort. Therefore, they will need a heavily armed troop of mounted men. Gathering the men will not be an issue, but additional payment will be required given the risk of encounter with colonial militia. Galloway provides Moses an additional five guineas to cover expenses and offers ten more if the horses and baggage reach Princeton safely.

Moses agrees without hesitation, knowing thirty gold guineas are well worth the risk and less a week of travel. Galloway states, "Thomlinson will be notified to expect your men after midnight this coming Sabbath, and you should meet me here, at Princeton Common, by midday on Monday, May 6. Thomlinson will ensure that additional flatboats are available at Yardley's Ferry. Commandeer the necessary boats, but do not kill anyone without necessity, and use coin to pay the tolls." Once in New Jersey, Moses is instructed to come up the Pike to Princeton. "I will have additional armed riders meet you west of Maidenhead," states Galloway. The prospect of easy gold has Abraham and Moses quickly on the road back toward Bull's Island and Tory's Ferry. Jacob's braves and the Plumstead Doan boys provide the manpower required for the escort.

The Doan gang arrives in Newtown as agreed. They meet Robert Robersen from Lower Bucks, whom Thomlinson introduces as a friend, "Not unknown to banditry, horse theft and violence." Robersen has arranged for a smooth crossing at Yardley, and Galloway is delighted when the party arrives safely in Princeton by midday. Over the next few months, the Doan and Robersen gangs steal dozens more horses and commit highway robbery, primarily against colonial government tax collectors. Meanwhile, Galloway pays Moses, via his cutout Thomlinson, to spy on the American colonial forces in and around Pennsylvania, New Jersey and New York.

A Land Worth Fighting For

CHAPTER TWO

SCENE 1

A Spy is Born of Fighting Spirit

Christ's Church • Philadelphia • five months prior • early December, 1775

ELIZABETH "BETSY" ROSS NÉE GRISCOM waits alone outside Christ Church to speak with her late husband's uncle, George Ross, following a service. Betsy and her young husband, John Ross, are married only a few short years. The young couple started an upholstery business together, and they made flags for the large Philadelphia Navy given Uncle George's connections. Betsy left her family and Quaker society behind to marry a member of the Church of England but is happily married. John's death truly leaves her at a loss, and she is angry. John, an officer in the militia, is killed just a few weeks prior. Tory sappers, loyal to the king, ignite casks of black powder that are being guarded by John's company on the Philadelphia docks.

George Ross exits the church with Robert Morris. Both men are Pennsylvania representatives to the Continental Congress and future signers of the Declaration of Independence come July. Morris is a close friend of General Washington, and he is the primary financial backer of the Continental Army. George Ross approaches Betsy with open arms, introducing her to Morris, explaining, "My niece has been inconsolable since the death of my nephew and would perform any service to avenge his killing by faithless Tories." Betsy's patriotic zeal is matched by her intelligence, and Morris promises to introduce her to General Washington. Morris asks Betsy to be patient, attend to her business, as Washington may devise a use for her on return from Boston.

By mid spring of 1776, Betsy arranges through Jenkintown merchants to secure a consistent supply of quality wool to be woven into bunting fabric for production of flags and military uniforms. She plans a visit with her mother's sister, in provincial Quakertown, as her Germantown fabric supplier deals with many of the wool growers in northern Bucks County. Congress is making provision for a larger, more professional army, and Betsy's business is a direct beneficiary. After a successful trip, Betsy returns to Philadelphia a few weeks prior to Washington's victorious return from Boston.

General Washington previously takes command of the colonial militias forming the newly created Continental Army, when he rides, sword in hand, in front of the troops gathered near Harvard College on July 3, 1775. All New England and colonies as far away as Virginia are represented on the Common that day. Companies of marksmen, with rifles, join Washington from Pennsylvania, Maryland and Virginia. The German rifling technology, imported and perfected in the previous century by Pennsylvania immigrants, quickly becomes the scourge of a British army unprepared for its range and accuracy.

Britain has struggled to exert her financial or mercantile control over the Massachusetts Bay region. The Boston Tea Party in December 1773 crosses a line for King George III and his mercantile partner, the East India Company. By 1775, British forces garrisoned within Boston have increased by thousands. British General Thomas Gage is empowered to disband the local government, disarm local militias and close off Boston's port to all shipping under discretion of the 1774 Boston Port Act; one of the "Intolerable Acts," passed by the British Parliament to coerce the rebellious colony's submission.

Gage kicks the hornet nest and citizen minutemen militia rise up in response. A full brigade of British regulars set out, on a not so secret mission, to capture a rebel arsenal thought to exist at Concord, more than a dozen miles from Boston. The brigade is thwarted by organized militia units and is subsequently mauled by thousands of citizens who come out to fire upon them as they retreat toward Boston. General Gage sparks a popular uprising, and the accountants of Whitehall, whose calculations primed the policies at the heart of the revolution, could not know the bill for the damage that will ensue to King George's empire. Thousands, maybe tens of thousands of armed and organized patriots descend upon Boston, besieging the city, and bottle up British forces within the Boston Peninsula. No matter, the English double down. Generals Howe and Clinton arrive with reinforcements from England, and in late June 1775, a few weeks prior to Washington's arrival, the

British lose their last chance to prevent a provincial skirmish from exploding into global conflict.

Across the harbor, north of Boston, patriot militia has fortified the hills above Charlestown before the British can seize them. The threat mobilizes the British commanders, who are forced into action. On June 17 they ferry more than three thousand assault troops to the peninsula and take back the hills. The battle of Bunker Hill is a Pyrrhic victory. General Gage likely informs General William Howe that colonial militia display extraordinary fighting spirit, atypical to the British experience during the prior French and Indian war. Howe will experience this personally, however, on Breed's Hill, as a third of his soldiers are turned into casualties and an extraordinarily high number of his officers are killed or wounded by colonial marksmen.

The Americans atop Bunker and Breed's hills display a willingness to stand and fight against massed columns of professional soldiers. The battle should have given the king pause to reconsider the royal approach to the conflict. A prideful duty instead emerges, and General Howe is promoted.

The promotion says much about the king and his council. For the king, Howe's noble blood and willingness to put men in harm's way proves him the correct man for the task at hand. A king's task is to bring his subjects to heel, no matter the cost in blood or treasure.

Upon arrival in Boston, Washington begins the long process of coalescing a disparate set of colonial militias into an organized fighting team, a modern army. In one form, however, his army is more advanced than that of General Howe's. Washington knew the frontier well, and he is adamant that the Continental Congress provision Special Forces units of rifle wielding marksmen. Most boys on the frontier are taught how to shoot a rifle for hunting and defense. This pool of trained killers, who bring their own specialized weapons to the fight, is one of America's great resources in the struggle against tyranny.

Riflemen help prevent the British from showing their heads outside Boston, and Howe's movement is compromised. When soldiers from Vermont, Massachusetts and Connecticut surprise British forces on Lake Champlain, capturing fort Ticonderoga, the British position in Boston is fatally compromised. The Americans capture more than a hundred cannon, and General Washington sends Henry Knox, a bookseller who will become America's first Secretary of War, to bring back as many as possible to Boston. In a Herculean effort, Knox has cannon pushed, pulled and drug back to Boston in winter, and emplaced on the Dorchester Heights overseeing Boston Harbor.

General Howe reacts quickly, before his shipping lifeline is threatened. The siege of Boston has made the city a desperate position for the British. A smallpox epidemic is stoked by the siege in the winter of 1775–1776. Although many Englishmen have acquired immunity to the disease, colonists and much of Washington's army suffer greatly. Once Knox's guns are in place, however, Boston is a potential killing field for the British. Howe evacuates the town, sailing his soldiers, and any loyal subjects who can find ship, up to Fort Halifax, Nova Scotia, in Canada.

The British abandon Boston mid March 1776, and by early April Washington is back on the road south. His newly organized army begins preparations to defend an exposed New York City and the Hudson River Valley, while the general heads for the Continental Congress in Philadelphia. He reaches the city before the end of May.

Stars & Stripes

George Washington is in Philadelphia barely a week, yet he already prepares to join the bulk of his army in Manhattan. As Commander and Chief, the general still harbors personal doubt. As a leader of men, however, he is world-class, a born executive, able to judge character, solve logistical challenge and delegate authority. He is committed and will continually show the personal bravery, indeed cunning, necessary to defeat the royal goliath in combat.

Supporters of the king and spies remain within the capital. Reports of armed Tories, operating openly in Bucks County, are concerning for the general given the county's strategic location on the Delaware River. With this concern, Washington is on his way to meet with a young patriot, the upholsterer and widow Betsy Ross. A congressional committee, formed to design and produce a new unified flag for the American Continental Army, consists of George Ross, Robert Morris and the general.

Washington met Betsy earlier during church service and is impressed. However, the full committee is meeting with Betsy to discuss production of the flag at her home and business on Arch Street. As his carriage hustles down the cobbled streets, Washington hopes that George and Robert are correct, that Betsy may serve a higher purpose. The nation and army need a unifying flag, of course, but effective intelligence and counter espionage is critical, otherwise such a flag may enjoy a short life.

General Washington enters the house and is immediately greeted warmly by Betsy. Boarders and workers look on in astonishment as the general joins the discussion on flags. Morris explains they have preliminarily settled on the thirteen alternating red and white stripes of the Grand Union Flag's field, as Betsy is already producing similar navy ensign. "Very well," the general replies, "However, I require a starry blue canton in similar form to my current headquarters flag." All agree the combination will make a fine standard, yet Betsy suggests the use of a five-pointed star rather than six. She explains that the change will speed up production and reduce cost. Being partial to his current standard, the general is unconvinced until Betsy, who has begun making multiple folds of a piece of cloth, snips the folded cloth once and holds up a perfect five-pointed star for his inspection.

Duly impressed, Washington asks rhetorically, "What other wizardry do you perform, Madam?" Having earlier been briefed by her uncle while walking home from church, Betsy replies, *"Herr General, ich weiß dass Ihre Gedanken eine von König Georg bezahlte Armee betreffen, die auf unsere Küsten zusteuert."* George Ross is not aware his niece speaks fluent German, and he bids her translate the response. Betsy continues, "General, I know your thoughts concern a German army, paid by King George, headed for our shores." General Washington's mild astonishment turns to a wry smile as the three men realize Betsy is not just a businesswoman or patriot, but a potential weapon of war.

CHAPTER THREE

SCENE 1

Heights of Guan

Preparation for Battle • Staten Island, New York • summer 1776

PRIOR TO HIS ARREST, WILLIAM FRANKLIN, the previous royal governor of New Jersey, has instructed a network of spies and loyal Delaware Indians to continue providing intelligence to British forces in the region. Galloway relies on this network, and he is informed that General Washington has deployed a strong defensive force along the Heights of Guan in Brooklyn. The Battery, lower Manhattan, is the American base of operations, and both the Hudson and East River approaches to the island are heavily fortified to deter amphibious assault. The East River divides the American Continental Army. Galloway, an intelligent man with a soldier's eye for tactical advantage, devises a new mission for the Doan boys.

By early July 1776, Moses Doan and other Tory operators and opportunists have been ferrying horses and additional supplies into Staten Island for months. On the third day of July, a large British fleet begins disembarking the British army under General William Howe on Staten Island. Galloway, who has relocated to Staten Island, requests Moses meet him at the Billopp estate. Tens of thousands of British and German troops set up camp on the island, and Galloway tasks Moses with a reconnaissance mission across the harbor.

Lower New York harbor bristles with the masts of British warships as Moses and Jacob land on Long Island, at the eastern end of Jamaica Bay, on a mid-August evening. Their mission is not complicated. The pair will travel a slow arc, counterclockwise, until near Little Neck Bay, at which point they will travel westerly toward Bushwick, above the ridges, while observing the strength of the Continental Army and the potential approaches.

Colonel Billopp has provided Moses a code word that is shared with General Howe and his designated forward commander, Henry Clinton. Moses is instructed to return well within a fortnight and provide intelligence to Howe or Clinton. Jacob's knowledge of Long Island allows the men to limit human contact, bivouacking for days, until they approach the heights above Flatbush and observe the tactical formations defending the approaches. To their surprise, the easterly passes are lightly guarded by a few battalions, over miles of ridge, while four or five regiments man the pass above Flatbush. Confronted by a cavalry cornet, Moses claims they have come from eastern Connecticut to help build defensive works, and the two spies are put to work chopping trees along the ridge for chevaux-de-frise.

In the days that follow, they confirm the passes to the east are manned by no more than a weak regiment, without defensive works. Most important, they understand that the Jamaica Pass is not fortified and guarded by a small cavalry detachment alone. The same night word reaches the ridge of British troops landing in Brooklyn, Moses and Jacob slip away headed for Jamaica Pass. Jacob knows an old Indian trail skirting just east of the pass. The two men easily avoid a small company of light cavalry, up the pass, and steal horses belonging to patrons at Howard's Tavern near the bottom. Armed with the most important intelligence of the young war, Jacob and Moses head quickly west for General Clinton's army.

The British begin ferrying troops across to Gravesend, Brooklyn, during the previous day, Aug. 22, 1776. One of the largest amphibious operations in the history of the Western Hemisphere transpires in the lower New York harbor, between Staten Island and Brooklyn. British and German forces, as well as loyalist colonial militia, number more than forty thousand souls in the region. The British command a fleet of tall ships hundreds strong. Including HMS Eagle, at 64 guns, there are at least ten ships of the line carrying near six hundred cannons. A few dozen heavily armed frigates, akin to a modern destroyer, provide the British enough firepower to train hundreds of guns on Manhattan or Brooklyn with a portion of their fleet, winds and tides permitting. New York City, and the thousands of Continental American Army soldiers defending her, would likely have been unnerved if our modern twenty-four-hour news cycle existed during the late eighteenth century.

Moses and Jacob are corralled and escorted by mounted scout dragoons under Clinton's command. They reach British perimeter pickets by late morning on Aug. 23. General Clinton, with aid-de-camp, quickly debriefs Moses. Clinton sends dispatch to Howe, who confers aboard HMS Eagle with his brother, Admiral Richard Howe, and begins to devise an assault plan based on the intelligence provided. Jacob, waiting outside the field tents, overhears a number of British and German officers boastfully discussing the beating they plan to give the rebellious American "farmers," and exclaiming the frontier lands they hope to be promised by his grace, Lord Richard Howe, Gen. Howe's older brother, Admiral of the Fleet and the king's privy-council emissary to the American colonies. A handsomely attired Hessian commander, the Count Carl Emil Ulrich von Donop, rebukes his compatriots for their shortsighted goals, stating, "Much of the finest well watered and forested lands exist near the coasts or occupied cities." The count intends to win such fame and honor in the eyes of the king, "His majesty will gladly grant lands along the Delaware River, formerly sold by Quakers to the many wealthy rebel souls living in the province."

Before Jacob may check himself, he scoffs, sternly stating, "Not all men in the county are rebels!" A *jäger* sergeant, a man "hunter," guarding the count, quickly sends Jacob to a knee with a blow from a rifle butt, along with some choice words in German. The count yells out, *"Halt,"* and the sergeant stiffen to attention. An apology, meant to sooth Jacob, calms the situation before a deadly confrontation ensues, however, Jacob has not let a man strike him, and live, since he was a boy in his mother and uncles' village. Moses exits Clinton's tent at that moment and calls out for Jacob, allowing the count to quickly surmise the connection with Clinton's spy.

Count von Donop places a hand on Jacob's shoulder and approaches Moses, asking whether the two men are Pennsylvanian scouts. Moses notes the mild Germanic accent and quickly replies, "Upper Bucks." The count, with a quick glance at Jacob, feigns confusion and asks, "Were not the Delaware Indians removed from the county after the 1737 walking purchase?" The question takes both men by surprise, and Jacob, although still mad, is now intrigued. Before he can answer, Moses waves him off and replies, "Most of the tribe had moved north of the county by that date, but a few of Jacob's clan stayed. Why is it of concern to you?" The count simply replies, "I'd heard the land was stolen." "We were not helpless children," shouts Jacob, though he himself had been a very young child, and Moses explains, "There were few large villages left at the time and the Mohawk chose to support the brothers' Penn claim, as English allies, rather than the Lenape they had previously conquered."

The count simply nods his understanding, but he also understands the men may prove valuable to him beyond the bounds of the current conflict. Reaching into a leather satchel, Colonel von Donop produces a small purse of silver coin. He hands the purse to Moses, saying, "For the man's inconvenience, and please keep me informed of the county to the extent that you may be able." The count quickly takes his leave, with Moses somewhat astonished, and Jacob both angry and confounded. Moses, seeing the look on Jacob's face, drops the silver into his hand and says, "Good work," as they both begin to laugh.

SCENE 2

Hold the Line, Cometh the King

Battle of Brooklyn • Long Island, New York • August 27, 1776

Three days later, at nine o'clock in the evening, the main British force, approximately ten thousand strong, strikes out east under Henry Clinton. The troops slip south of Flatbush, Long Island, under the cover of night. They head for Howard's Tavern, at the eastern end of the heights. The British leave campfires burning and enough troops that American Continental forces do not realize the departure.

After midnight an additional five thousand British troops, under General James Grant, begin to probe the western American defenses up the road between the Gowanus Bay and the Heights of Guan, near today's Green Wood Cemetery. Grant attacks, pinning down the American right flank, as colonial commanders believe this to be the primary British assault. Pennsylvania Muskets and Riflemen are some of the first large units to trade standing fire with British forces, while Brigadier William Alexander, "Lord" Stirling, reinforces the American right with fewer than three full regiments, consisting of units from the 1st Delaware and 1st Maryland primarily.

The British flank the colonials by taking a hill east of the Gowanus road, but a force including Pennsylvania riflemen take back the hill with a brutal counterattack. American soldiers kill the commander of the maneuver, British Colonel James Grant. Confusion reigns, as the American's believe the dead officer is General Grant. Euphoria exists briefly, at the top of Battle Hill, before the Americans realize they are trapped.

British military forces are the world's finest in the late eighteenth century, but some of the most experienced professional troops under General Howe's command are German, principally from the Landgraviate of Hesse-Kassel. Known as Hessians, many of these soldiers have cut their teeth fighting in wars across Europe, from the Russian Crimea to the Scottish Highlands. Though a small German principality, Hesse-Kassel keeps a very high portion of adult males under arms. The principality's primary economy is war and its ruler, Frederick II, expands his wealth by lending soldiers to foreign leaders, notably his nephew, King George III of Great Britain.

On the morning of August 27, five thousand of these foreign Hessian warriors wait at the bottom of Flatbush Pass, well east of Battle Hill, lead by their General von Heister. The Americans at the top earlier send reinforcements west to Lord Stirling and have less than three full regiments opposing the Germans. Hessian cannon fire successfully holds the remaining American forces stationary on top of the pass. Miles farther northeast of the Hessian position, near the Evergreen Cemetery, General Howe is preparing to slam the trap door shut on the Americans. General Clinton's advance units reach Howard's Tavern, near Jamaica Pass, in the early morning hours. Howe forces William Howard and his teenaged son to guide the British up the old Indian trail, skirting the pass undetected, and surprise the few mounted American officers on guard. The Americans surrender without firing a shot or sending a warning.

Before nine in the morning, Howe has ten thousand rested soldiers ready to march west, trapping the Americans between the Germans and the East River. The British fire cannon from the top of Jamaica Pass, and the Hessians begin their assault on the hills above Flatbush. Outnumbered almost ten to one, the American forces along the ridges are enveloped and rolled up into northwest Brooklyn.

THE DOAN GANG HANDS THE BRITISH THEIR FIRST MAJOR VICTORY AGAINST THE AMERICANS.

The American patriots continue to fight. The smaller unit guarding the eastern heights flees the tide of redcoats, however, the American center under

General John Sullivan pivots to hold off Clinton and Howe while delaying the Hessian assent. The Hessians eventually overwhelm, bayoneting through the thin American lines. No quarter is given, and the Hessians execute surrendering common soldiers. Bravery and competent tactical leadership save the rebellion. As hand-to-hand fighting rages, General Sullivan salvages a successful tactical retreat from the ashes of defeat.

Thousands of British Marines land and reinforce Grant's attack on the American right prior to noon. Nevertheless, Lord Stirling prevents the British from closing the pincer on the American right, thereby enabling Sullivan's partial escape. As remaining American forces retreat behind a fortified Brooklyn Heights, on the East River, Lord Stirling's men are forced to show a soldiers' heroism. Trapped by Hessian and British forces attacking from their rear and east flank, Stirling's remaining soldiers, mostly men from Maryland and Delaware, are forced to wade across the Gowanus Creek/Marsh near the Old Stone House. Many men reach the safety of fortified positions between Red Hook & Brooklyn Heights.

LIKE SPARTANS OF OLD, at least 300 Maryland regulars are ordered to stand and fight a rear-guard action while thousands of enemy soldiers close on their position. The entire Maryland unit is killed counter attacking at the Stone House, while Lord Stirling, sword in hand, fights his way through British forces to Hessian troops lead by **THE COUNT!**

SCENE 3
Demos Kratos

Battle of Brooklyn • Long Island, New York • Eve of Battle 1776

Prior to the battle, Colonel von Donop gives strict instruction to his subordinate officers that no quarter be given to any American fighting without a sword in hand. The message is crystal clear, only officers of note should be taken alive. The common soldier is to be executed, and Hessian soldiers know to head such orders on pain from the lash. The count intends to help make the war as short as possible, and he has seen brutality proven effective in continental European conflicts. This will not be his last misjudgment of the fiercely independent, largely middle-class soldiers who stand above his position. Many of the men facing off against Colonel von Donop represent the highest common standard of living worldwide, and the Americans mean to keep it that way.

The evening before battle, General von Heister orders the count's grenadier regiments and personal corps of field *jäger* to lead the assault on the Americans atop the pass. The grenadier regiment under Colonel Johann Rahl will support the count in reserve position. Colonel Rahl and the count's lives have been intertwined for decades. Their common competitiveness, if not mutual contempt, will be utilized with mixed success by German and British generals during the early war.

Advancement in the professional Hessian army is understandably, primarily, via merit. The count's family served as military leaders and confidants of their prince for decades; however, and Carl Emil Ulrich von Donop has been on a fast track since the day of his birth. Johann Rahl's father had been an officer in the Donop family regiments, and Johann was promoted to junior officer before Carl von Donop reached his teens. Now fifty, Colonel Rahl has fought in every major European continental war of the previous three decades. He is well respected by the soldiers under his command. A jäger captain, who later rises to the rank of general, indicates that none of the other German officers is fit to carry Rahl's sword[1]. History shows Johann Rahl to be tough, brave, but maybe a bit too prideful and overconfident in his experience.

---

[1] Captain Johann Ewald; *Diary of the American War: A Hessian Journal* (Yale University Press, 1979)

Dining on Mutton, General von Heister's officers are in high spirits and eager for the battle to come in the morning. Colonel Rahl has been observing Count von Donop closely. General von Heister has confided in Rahl that he means to test the mettle of Colonel von Donop's regiments early in the campaign. Rahl and von Donop served together in the Crimea for the German born Empress, Catherine of Russia, a few years previous. Rahl knows von Donop possesses the bravery of a man more willing to die than be dishonored. Johann Rahl is not jealous. Count von Donop's aggressive ambition will serve well in the coming assault. Rahl's prince, Frederick II, has personally awarded him command of his own regiment, titled with the Rahl surname. In fact, Frederick sends Johann Rahl to America based on Rahl's loyalty, leadership ability, and the high regard English leaders have for his experience. Rahl's bravery is proven early in his career, while helping the English crush the Scottish highlanders at the Battle of Culloden.

Sensing the mood, General von Heister turns from his feast and states, "Speaking of Scots, the highland regiments under Lord Cornwallis look frothing to kill their cousins." The noble Colonel von Hachenburg mentions the smart tartans worn by the 42nd Highlanders under Colonel Thomas Stirling. Turning to Rahl, von Hachenburg asks, "Do you remember the Black Watch with such a gleam, colonel?" "My memories are of tartans stained as though a surgeon's rag," admits Colonel Rahl, "But I have no doubt as to the bravery of these Scots." Hachenburg, partly in jest, asks whether an opposing commander, William Alexander, who styles himself "Lord Stirling," is cousin to the British officer. General von Heister chimes in, "The only person a highlander would rather fight, than an Englishman, is his own cousin." All laugh heartily, but Rahl addresses Count von Donop directly, "Carl, if you capture Stirling tomorrow his family may finance your ambitions with a ransom." It pains the count to acknowledge Rahl, whom he has disliked since a boy, unable to demand the older man's deference. Colonel von Donop acknowledges the thoughtful truth, however, as William Alexander is the male blood heir to the Scottish Earldom of Stirling and yet denied the title by order of the English Parliament in London.

William Alexander, Lord Stirling, is an American. He is born in New York to a Whig lawyer and a mercantilist mother. In fact, Lord Stirling and his mother are partners and are two of the wealthiest private business owners in the region. The count knows he can rise no higher within the rigid European nobility. His young son will securely inherit his lands and title, but Carl von Donop desires more. Ironic, he wishes to develop the personal wealth American freedoms have provided families like William Alexander's.

England is the center of a dynamic global empire, with London at the heart of global integrated economic systems. England cannot nearly meet the raw material needs of its growing industries, as well the maintenance of a large portion of the world's military and mercantile shipping fleets. During the late eighteenth century, British shipyards import thousands of wooden masts annually from the Russian Empire[2]. Even when Russia and Britain are technically at war, the commerce barely slows. Russian hemp, iron, as well as other raw and semi-finished products flood into English shipyards and factories. England's current account is negatively affected by the deficits generated, and as America today, investment, services, and other revenues help counteract the unbalanced trade in commodities. Such "services" prevent too much English gold from filling the coffers of Catherine the Great and her Russian successors.

Count von Donop understands the Revolutionary War is simply about who will control, and ultimately financially benefit from, the enormous resources of the North American continent and her industrious colonists. Russia is essentially a slave state, with millions of feudal serfs providing economic benefit to a small slice of the society. The American colonies can't compete with the Russian geography and low labor costs in industries like iron production and some agricultural products. The count experienced Russia first-hand and believes change will come at the hands of enlightened monarchs. He thinks African slave labor can grow in the northern colonies as it has in the southern. The scale of such labor may not reach that of South America or the West Indies, but enough to compete more effectively for European import markets.

The southern colonies generate a sizable trade surplus with Great Britain, largely due cash crops like tobacco and indigo worked by slaves. The northern colonies run a much larger trade deficit. The Quakers of Pennsylvania are mostly self-sufficient, but the hardscrabble farmers and fisherman near Boston have little to tempt British investors and consumers. New Englanders

---

[2] Alfred W. Crosby, Jr.; *America, Russia, Hemp and Napoleon: American Trade with Russia and the Baltic, 1783–1812* (Ohio State University Press, 1965)

purchase British goods heavily with colonial paper money, primarily issued by land banks, but Whitehall spent a vast horde of gold defending New England in the French & Indian War and look increasingly to tax the colony. In 1751, the British institute a "Currency Act" restricting New England's ability to open new public banks and issue paper money. England's merchant class desire not being paid in colonial "script", and in 1764 the policy of not allowing such paper to be used for private transactions extends to all thirteen colonies. Ben Franklin believes the policy reduces economic growth, helps to spread poverty and largely causes the American Revolution.

The less wealthy New Englanders keenly feel any increase in taxation such that they organize a militia, able to withstand the royal army, handing the British defeat in the first campaign of the revolution. New England patriots chase the British army and fleet out of Boston and up to Nova Scotia in March 1776. The victory paves the way for the Continental Congress, in Philadelphia, to sign the Declaration of Independence prior to Howe's invasion of Brooklyn. Democratic government quickly makes its boldest move forward in more than two thousand years.

Interesting note: A few short decades in the future while George Washington is America's first President, he pushes for the fledgling American Navy to domestically design and build, in Boston no less, a squadron of "Super" frigates. The new American vessels hunt down and destroy the pride of the British Admiralty, her vast global fleet of mid-sized warships. Her massive ships of the line allow Britain to fight strategic heavyweight battles with the fleets of her ancient European enemies, but it is British frigates that patrol and maintain her global economic empire.

Common Law provides Englishman some historical defense against military conscription. However, as the American Revolution wears on, the British experiment with the ancient practice, a practice many think akin to slavery. The practice blossoms with the British Navy, as her global fleet requires large numbers of skilled sailors, especially during the Napoleonic Wars. British warships continually raid American merchantmen on the high seas, impressing sailors into British naval service. Such conscription, or forced labor, causes outrage in the American populace, and the practice helps lead to the outbreak of a second Anglo-American war in 1812.

Prior to the War of 1812, American ingenuity, oak and iron produce ships able to dominate enemies found alone on the high seas. The British are forced to order her frigates to flee the new American hunters, such as the USS Constitution, nicknamed "Old Ironsides," until and unless they encounter them in squadron strength. Like an immortal light heavy-weight champion, who has never been beaten, USS Constitution sits in Boston Harbor still, commissioned and ready to fight the ghosts of enemies past.

From the Halls of Montezuma
To the shores of Tripoli;
We fight our country's battles
On the land as on the sea...

CHAPTER FOUR

SCENE 1

The Sacrifice

Escape from New York • August to November 1776

AS HIS COUNTRYMEN CONTINUE TO REGALE each other over dinner and speculate on the battle to come in the morning, Colonel von Donop is deep in thought and pictures the wooded hills and fertile fields of eastern Pennsylvania. He is thinking about the famous Durham Furnace, on the Upper Delaware River, one of the oldest stock companies in the colony. He wonders whether he can acquire the asset, profitably export bar iron and finished goods such as cannon, rifles and shot back to Europe. A pursed smile forms as he thinks of a new title, *The Iron Count.* Sharp iron is just what his battle-hardened soldiers will present the rebels in the morning. Most of Howe's soldiers in New York aren't English. Nearly half are Germans and many remaining soldiers are from Scotland. "A man of iron will may forge great opportunity in this new world," the count whispers to himself.

The British are globally overextended and require foreign troops to help crush Washington. A man able to organize and arm a large province like Pennsylvania may carve a kingdom for himself. Separate treaties with the indigenous population will be required, of course, but thousands of European soldiers and veterans, desirous of land and wealth, can easily be imported for this new kingdom. The count knows his family will never leave Europe, but he thinks it a small matter. He plans for Frederick's heirs to view his new iron kingdom as an ally, and of course he can always start a new family.

Before noon the following day, Colonel von Donops's regiments decimate American forces under General Sullivan, regroup and begin chasing the rebels along ridges toward the Gowanus marshes. The Americans retreat more orderly than expected and continue to provide resistance. Finally, with Grant, von Donop and Cornwallis surrounding the rebel forces on three sides, the Americans again surprise. A sacrificial holding force repeatedly attacks Cornwallis' relatively fresh troops with such savage fury that the remaining rebels escape through the marshes. Remnants of this American holding force fight hand-to-hand with Scots and Hessian infantry, trying to evade death or capture, while *jäger* marksmen pick off lone rebel soldiers from a safe distance.

The count's attention is drawn to screams from a felled horse, and he witnesses a scene the likes of which he's dreamt throughout his years fighting. A dismounted American officer shoots a highlander point blank with pistol while parrying another's bayonet thrust with his sword. Red clad soldiers rush the man, and his desperation is belied by an obvious energetic skill and determination not to die. "No," the count thinks aloud. He realizes the man is not trying to escape but heading for the Hessian lines. Field *jäger* guarding the count are alert, and one man takes steady aim on the American officer with his rifle. As the *jäger* fires the count moves quickly, directing the shot into the ground with a slash from his saber. With a loud command in German, to take the man prisoner, a dozen grenadiers surround the officer with pointed bayonets gleaming in the sun. Addressing the captured man directly in English, the count yells out, "Lord Stirling, may I please have your sword." The tone and recognition help William Alexander to regain some composure as he stabs the dirt and leans on the hilt of his sword. Recognizing his captor by reputation, Lord Stirling yells back, "My good count, a minute more and I surely would have suffered the fate of Richard Plantagenet." Taking possession of the sword, the count responds, "Dear sir, you are worth more than he."

General Howe must have felt he could force an American surrender in the morning, as he did not press his gains, and dug in rather than assault Brooklyn Heights the same day. The result, according to many, is Devine providence. The following day, a Nor'easter rolls in and prevents the British fleet from forcing an East River entry or cutting off Washington's ability to regroup in lower Manhattan. As the winds die down on the night of August 29, nine thousand remaining American troops begin evacuating their trenches under cover of darkness and are ferried across the mile-wide East River by experienced Massachusetts' soldier mariners. The next morning, an eerie fog falls over Brooklyn, allowing the last Americans, including General

Washington, to row across to Manhattan unchallenged. When the fog lifts, assaulting British forces are confronted with empty trenches.

Over the coming months the British and her allies hound the American Continental Army out of Manhattan and New York altogether. In a final injury born of Washington's deference to his subordinate commanders from New England, the remaining American troops in Manhattan, nearly three thousand strong, are captured trying to defend the Hudson River from within the fortified heights above Harlem. Once again, the British attack with tactical brilliance and large numbers of highly experienced troops. Colonel Rahl shows his bravery, leading his regiment up steep rocky terrain to overwhelm battalions of American sharpshooters and artillery defending Fort Washington. The Hessians prove their valor and worth to the British crown with heavy casualties. While **MARGARET CORBIN**, an American beacon, displays heroism ably manning an artillery piece aimed at Rahl's Hessians, replacing her husband killed earlier during the battle.

Prior to the battle for control of the Heights, General Washington's forces number well more than fifteen thousand. Over the next few weeks, the American Continental Army begins to hemorrhage manpower as it retreats south toward Trenton, harried by British forces under Lord Cornwallis. By the second week of December, Continental forces cross the Delaware River into the relative safety of Bucks County, Pennsylvania, and are under the watchful eyes of the Doan gang and the numerous Tories among a generally patriotic populace. American morale reaches a nadir, as enlistments are ending with the year, and desertions mount. In less than six weeks, battle losses and attrition cut the strength of Washington's army by more than two thirds. The Revolution hangs by a thread, and the newborn nation requires a miracle to survive.

SCENE 2

Guerrilla War

Central New Jersey • early December 1776

As Washington's remaining forces flee across the Delaware River, with a superior Cornwallis in pursuit, the British General sends dispatch to William Howe in New York, detailing the Continental Army's predicament. Cornwallis does not believe the Americans are able to field an offensive capability, either in the immediate future or come spring. The general, Lord Cornwallis, recommends General Grant take over his command of all royal forces in New Jersey and also requests immediate passage to England be booked for him and his retinue. Lord Cornwallis believes the American Revolution is finished, and he wishes to be the first courtier to bend the knee before his prince with the glad tidings.

The Count von Donop is vexed by General James Grant's ascendancy. Grant has already informed his Hessian counterpart that he will deploy royal forces in a garrison strategy, from Bordentown to Trenton, Princeton to Edison and Staten Island. Hessian regiments will man the posts in Trenton and southern Jersey most exposed to guerrilla tactics by local militia. Adding insult, Grant has allowed Colonel Rahl an independent command in Trenton, over the count's objections, though Colonel von Donop will retain nominal command in the south.

William Alexander travels south with Colonel von Donop. A regiment of highlanders has been attached to the count's command, and Lord Stirling has mixed feelings with his company. The count has guaranteed Lord Stirling's safe return to Washington's army, and he has arranged with Lord Stirling's mother, against William's protest, for a "reward." William's mother, his business partner, has transferred four thousand gold guineas to New York agents of the Frankfurt am Main merchant and private bank representing Count von Donop's interests. A surety bond for an additional six thousand guineas has been executed, such that the Frankfurt agents agreed to commit their European principles to a line of credit in the amount of fifty thousand gold guineas, capitalizing a new share company controlled by Count von Donop.

Proceeds from the loan must be used to purchase land, as collateral, within Bucks County and secondarily within twenty-five miles north or south of the Tohickon Creek and Delaware River confluence. The Count has avoided any complications with the British, regarding extortion on the exchange of an enemy officer, as Lord Stirling's family freely enters into the agreement. Lord Stirling's mother, the primary brains of the family business, knows a twenty percent ownership in a company that will purchase producing properties in Bucks County is an efficient hedge given the vagaries of war and Count von Donop's connections.

Carl von Donop sends word requesting Moses Doan meet his forces near Bordentown, New Jersey. Colonial militias in Hunterdon County are disrupting the supply lines south of Princeton. In fact, guerrilla activity has been highly aggressive from both sides of the Delaware River. Strung out over more than fifty miles, royal forces are being continually harassed and ambushed. Realizing that the depth of fighting spirit in the population will likely keep Washington and the revolution alive much longer than the British expect, the count sees an opportunity to solve his current tactical disadvantage while serving his own personal strategic aims and those of King George.

Moses and his cousin Abraham arrive in Bordentown a few days after Colonel von Donop. Moses is unhappy. Thomlinson had been paying the Doan gang, on behalf of Galloway and Howe, thirty guineas on the first Sunday of each month. Nevertheless, payments stop, and Thomlinson is in arrears, claiming Galloway ceased operations due the Americans' near defeat. Robersen, who still spies for Thomlinson, informs Moses that Galloway is trying to lower his profile. Galloway's wife, Grace, remains in Philadelphia trying to prevent the Continental Congress from confiscating properties, including the Durham Ironworks, held in her name as well as her Tory husband. The Continental Congress has no proof Grace shares her husband's loyalty to King George.

The count instructs Moses to visit a Philadelphia law office he is in correspondence with. A land agreement delineating an option price on a future purchase and sale agreement has been drawn up, and Moses will act as von Donop's agent. He will deliver payment of the option price. The contract will commit Grace Galloway to sell the Durham Ironworks and all associated mines, timbered, planted or fallow acreage, as well as associated buildings and equipment. All properties owned and controlled by Durham in the neighboring riverside towns is included as well.

Grace will receive an immediate payment of seventy guineas, satisfying the option price, and will receive an additional four hundred and thirty guineas if the count's group, the "Fidelia Land Company," executes the option in the coming three years. Grace Galloway is unaware of the arrangement, and she will be summoned once Moses reaches the law office. Moses will persuade Grace Galloway that the transaction is fair and reasonable given the deteriorating value of colonial paper money and the fact that the properties may be wrested from her control via other means. Providing false witness, as to her participation in her husband's spy ring, will be a simple matter. Carl von Donop is aware Mrs. Galloway will know Moses by reputation, and he is confident the transaction will be affected smoothly. Moses and Abraham are paid thirty guineas, as the count desires they work directly for him going forward. However, beyond a monthly retainer, the count woos the cousins with the opportunity to earn equity in his future land deals. Abraham is tasked with a sensitive mission to be executed while Moses is busy with Mrs. Galloway. The count will pay an additional hundred guineas if Abraham and the Doan gang can provoke an attack in force on Rahl's position in Trenton. Such an attack will provide impetus for the count to petition General Howe, recommending an immediate assault on colonial forces across the Delaware River. Carl von Donop reminds Abraham, "Nothing may reduce land prices like an army in the field."

Lord Stirling is not privy to the count's machinations. However, he has picked up enough to realize Colonel von Donop is working his private and military interests in tandem. Freedom of movement allows William to witness the Doan cousins leave separately and in different directions. The Scottish soldier assigned to guard Lord Stirling inadvertently confirms the Doan cousins are spies. The afternoon Moses leaves for Philadelphia, the count and

Lord Stirling dine together. William inquires as to the count's plans regarding land purchases. Carl von Donop is in high spirits, and he only comments that his designs for the Upper Bucks have progressed significantly. The count believes his template is in place. With the help of Moses, he will begin cataloguing all large tracts of land in eastern and northern Bucks County by affiliation with king or Congress. Royal supporters should be easily swayed to sign "fair" purchase agreement options while the rebels hold the county. The Doan gang may prove useful in this endeavor as well. Once the war ends, and royal rule reestablished, the count believes he will be able to acquire many of the properties he targets through corrupt proscription.

Within a few days, Abraham gathers the Doan and Jacob's braves for a meeting with Robersen's men at Coryell's Ferry on the Old York Road. A dozen men or more, enough thinks Abraham for his devised plan. Abraham means to revisit Ringo's Tavern. The Son's of Liberty organize their guerrilla operations from the bar room and have a secret meeting, known to Abraham, before the midnight. Abraham has collected uniforms and equipment from the Germans, and he intends to bait the bloody scene. Well prior to midnight, the Doan and Robersen gangs have the tavern surrounded, while one of Robersen's men has earlier entered the bar. The planted man opens the front door with a stagger as shouts from within bid him go home. Holding the door just a few seconds provides Robersen an opportunity to enter, and he quickly stabs a man waiting to bar the door. Additional patriots are quickly shot while sitting at the bar. Aaron and Mahlon enter the bar room with bayonets affixed to their muskets, and they move against a wall to cover the room. Abraham and Levi enter quickly behind with pistols and tomahawks in hand. A young militia leader attempts to retrieve a pistol from behind the bar, and Levi cleaves his skull with the tomahawk and points his own pistol at the next nearest rebel's head. As the wounded men emit the horrible sounds of death, Jacob and his Wolf clan braves enter the building from the rear, and they capture and execute all who attempt an escape.

Hannah Miller, the bar maid, recognizes Abraham and steps forward to spit on his face. Abraham, in reflex more than desire, smashes the woman's nose with a backhanded butt of a pistol while cursing loudly. Mahlon holds himself from laughter as Hannah calls them out as traitors, and staring at him with blue steel eyes, she shouts out, "You'll not laugh when the noose rounds your neck, boy." Abraham gives orders to bring all out on the front yard. Aaron smashes a German made musket on the bar, cracking the stock, then begins spilling rum on the floor before setting the room to blaze. Remaining militia leaders are quickly lined up against the outside wall and shot, while Robersen's men begin stabbing the bodies with the bayonet.

As the sounds of dying men abate, Abraham can still hear muffled screams. Turning toward Jacob, he states excitedly, "The woman, where is the woman?" Jacob and Abraham rush to the noise, behind a nearby shed, to witness one of Robersen's men trying to rape a near naked Hannah Miller. Hannah has been badly beaten and wears little more than a bloodied shift. Before the man can rise, Jacob smashes his jawbone with a rifle butt. Abraham pulls Jacob away from the shed, yelling, "I did not want this," but Jacob wrests away violently as he means to kill the man. For a matrilineal clan like Jacob's, killing a man of warrior age and killing a woman are separate. A musket shot rings out behind their heads, forcing the pair to the ground. Robert Robersen calmly takes in the scene, as a sobbing Hanna pulls herself up from the ground, and he stabs her through the belly with the bayonet. As an emotional shock wave stuns Jacob, Robersen produces a loaded pistol and tells both men to leave for Tory's Ferry. Reluctant, Abraham Doan ends Hannah's pain with the pistol.

SCENE 3

The Wolf of Brooklyn

Pineville • Bucks County, Pennsylvania • mid December 1776

Colonel von Donop has arranged for William Alexander to be rowed across the Delaware River to the safety of Bristol, Pennsylvania. By Sunday evening, December 15, William has caught up with Washington's moving headquarters off the Pineville Road. Entering the home on a chilly evening, he finds the general drinking Madeira wine in front of a fireplace with distinguished looking artillery officer. In fact, the young officer and Brig. General William Alexander are well acquainted. Washington exclaims, "Ah, William, I'm glad to see you safe," and turning toward Alexander Hamilton, states, "Captain Hamilton, I believe you know General Alexander." Saluting, Captain Hamilton concedes, "Yes of course, good to see you in whole, general." Captain Hamilton adds, "I hear Lord Cornwallis has taken to calling you the wolf of Brooklyn." William complains, "Simply so he does not have to acknowledge me, Lord Stirling." General Washington, amused for the first time in days, takes William by the arm and states, "Sir, none here shall call you lord either." Lord Stirling addresses Washington, "General, have you been more successful than I, convincing Captain Hamilton to forego battlefield glory for the greater good?" "Not at all, general," states Washington, "Captain Hamilton is not as yet my aide-de-camp."

The denial is simply a statement of formality as Alexander Hamilton already holds George Washington's confidence. The two have been discussing a potential attack on the Hessian garrison at Trenton. They agree artillery canister may be utilized to hem in the Germans, thereby foiling any counter-attack with the bayonet. Hamilton will serve a critical role in the attack on Trenton as a commander with New York artillery units. Given the current visit's provenance, General Washington feels it necessary for Hamilton to operate at arms length until the end of the campaign.

"William," asks Washington, "What is the disposition of Colonel von Donop's force?" Lord Stirling responds, "Near five brigades, including highlanders and field *jäger*, however, they are split unevenly between Trenton and Bordentown." Colonel Rahl has little more than three regiments and limited field artillery or cavalry. The count is wary of southern New Jersey militia, supported from Philadelphia, and feels able to support Rahl from Bordentown, a distance less half a dozen miles. Also, reports Lord Stirling, "The count holds Rahl in contempt for some unknown slight, and he may hesitate in his duty." General Washington responds, "Then gentlemen, we must endeavor to pull Colonel von Donop's forces south and detain him long enough that we may attack Rahl's regiments at Trenton while we still hold superior force."

"Nevertheless," exclaims Washington, "The fist order of business is to calm the Jersey militia." Captain Hamilton explains to Lord Stirling there are reports of a massacre in Hunterdon, with many militia leaders and patriots killed at a tavern on the Old York Road. A young woman has been reported defiled as well. "Defiled," asks Lord Stirling, and Hamilton replies, "Yes, and it looks to have been Hessian soldiers." Attached to the woman's body was a message that read, *"Ihr Bauern solltet wissen: Was ilr sät, ihr erntet."* Hamilton further explains that the message was pinned to the woman's body with the bayonet of a broken German musket. He translates the words as follows, "Ye farmers should know, ye reap what ye sow!"

The incident causes immediate retaliation from the populace of Hunterdon, and attacks against royal patrols increase. An unlucky company of Queen's Dragoons, commanded by the eldest son of Admiral Sir Francis Geary, is riding near Ringo's Tavern in the days following the massacre. Posted at Pennington, northwest of Trenton, the dragoons are headed to inspect an ordered supply of salted beef for their army, but the local militia is provided the schedule, ambushing the cavalry company as it rides through a wooded lane. Cornet Francis Geary is killed, his body never to be returned to England, and the blow hits home as the British limit reconnaissance and forage in the region.

Lord Stirling is uncomfortable. He has seen the discipline in the German ranks and is not convinced that either Rahl or the count would allow their men such latitude. Rape and murder are hallmarks of irregular forces, and he speaks up, "General, do you have reliable intelligence assets in the area that may confirm these reports?" Washington glances toward Hamilton and states, "We do general, but they are too valuable to compromise." Lord Stirling continues, "The militia leaders should be alerted that bolder action may prove counterproductive to our cause, and that they will await direct orders before engaging the enemy in force." Washington agrees, and again looking to Hamilton, states, "The good captain will be able to handle the issue going forward." Taking leave to seek lodging at the Pineville Inn, Lord Stirling asks Captain Hamilton to visit him in the morning. Smiling to himself, William Alexander thinks how quickly the prodigy, Alexander Hamilton, has made his mark. A spymaster with a field commission, Hamilton is now confidant to Washington, arguably the most important person in the Western Hemisphere. William knows Captain Hamilton would likely now be dead if he had served under him at Brooklyn.

Captain Hamilton has no intention of waiting till morning to visit the Inn, a few short miles up the road. Two old school friends from the West Indies await his arrival and instructions. The three will place in motion a plan that may change the outcome of the Revolutionary War and the cause of freedom for all mankind. Riding together under quite stars, Lord Stirling describes the men he saw working for Colonel von Donop. Hamilton does not recognize their description and will pass along the intelligence. The fact that Count von Donop may be working his own intelligence agents is highly interesting, if not unusual, however, Lord Stirling reveals that Colonel von Donop is engaged in a scheme to buy up land in Bucks County, and he is preparing to feather a nest for himself once the British take back control of the colony. William also outlines the company, Fidelia Land Co., that his mother has helped finance, and that the count has a fixation on the Durham Ironworks which is currently supplying badly needed ammunition to the Americans.

Alexander Hamilton is quite familiar with Lord Stirling's mother. Before leaving the island of St. Croix for Columbia College, the teenaged Hamilton was already helping to manage the books for well-known import and export merchants in the West Indies who dealt with Lord Stirling's family business in New York City. Hamilton thinks Colonel von Donop may be a formidable adversary, and asks, "Can you tell me anything more about the man's character or desires?" Lord Stirling responds, "There is a bravery bordering on arrogance, but the man is cunning and not to be underestimated. Also, I believe him highly deferential to the fairer sex and may show a weakness in such regard." In fact, adds Stirling, "The massacre you've described sounds more like the workings of Tory militia or something else all together. I believe either Colonel Rahl or Count von Donop would meet out swift justice to any soldiers leaving such a scene or that provocative message." Hamilton takes clear mental not of the advice.

Hamilton bids Lord Stirling a good evening as they reach the Pineville Inn. He is traveling farther to the Old York Road, in Buckingham proper, where Ephraim Johns and Moriah Strong are lodged and await his return. Ephraim was an African slave, working the sugar mills in Antigua, before burning his face so badly in a boiling house accident caused his master to sell him to the captain of an English privateer. Ephraim's natural intelligence and work ethic quickly turned him into a first-rate sailor and fighter. Ephraim and crewmates spent years taking prizes among Portuguese slavers and merchantmen plying the waters between Africa and Recife. Ephraim earned his freedom and was encouraged to attend school. Moriah Strong is the illegitimate daughter of a Dutch sugar merchant and a mother of mixed Black Carib heritage. Her mother taught her the healing arts, and she speaks five languages, including

Low German or Dutch. The surname truly reflects her character. In similarity with Alexander Hamilton, she survived the early death of her mother. This band of misfits spent their mid-teenage years attending a synagogue day school run by a Mistress Levy on the island of Nevis, the birthplace of Hamilton. The Anglican's refused education to all three, but no matter, they were educated together and make an effective team. The three old friends can read Hebrew to varying degree, and this provides a natural communications code for their tight spy network.

SCENE 4

Setting the Table

Buckingham • Bucks County, Pennsylvania • mid December 1776

Washington is enraged earlier in the fall of 1776. The British hung a young American officer who volunteered to stay behind enemy lines when the British took control of New York City. Nathan Hale was a Yale scholar and an early abolitionist thinker. The British claim he died well, and he is quoted stating, "I only regret that I have but one life to lose for my country." American soldiers and officers are repeatedly recounted as making comments of similar *Horatius* sentiment. The hanging of Nathan Hale, as an out-of-uniform officer, or spy, forces Washington to rely on civilians to perform his espionage. The British will come to regret their policy, as Washington will reciprocate during the war, notably hanging the multitalented and socially elegant Major John André as a result of the Benedict Arnold affair. In this environment, Hamilton has insured the general his connections with the British West Indian community in Philadelphia and New York will supply the required assets, and General Washington entrusts Hamilton with an asset of his own, the patriot widow Betsy Ross.

Based on Lord Stirling's intelligence, Captain Hamilton adjusts his plans. He will allow General Washington to send word directly for the Son's of Liberty to stand down in Hunterdon. Ephraim is preparing a large shipment of salted beef and pork with the farmers and merchants in Buckingham. The original plan is to ship the food up the Old York Road toward Raritan,

New Jersey. British forces still actively forage east of Edison, so the plan is for Ephraim to be captured by the British desperate for protein supplies. As a Black man and "English" sailor, he may infiltrate British camps.

The plan has now changed. Both Ephraim and Moriah will escort the wagons across the Delaware River and head southeast for Trenton and Colonel Rahl's command. They will present themselves as merchants who look to sell a consignment of food. When questioned by the Germans, the two will explain that they fled Bucks County since the colonial army is destitute of funds and may confiscate the consignment rather than pay the agreed price. The spies will offer the Hessians the foodstuffs at a discount, and they will agree to transport part of the consignment farther south to Colonel von Donop's brigades in Bordentown. Moriah will conceal her knowledge of German, allowing her to gather as much intelligence as possible. However, the primary mission is to sow disinformation in the minds of the Hessian commanders. The two spies will paint a picture of the American Continental Army, what few are left, as little more than a band of shoeless beggars, demoralized and counting the days until their enlistments end. The characterization isn't a whole lie, and this "truth" may lull the German's into a false sense of security.

Washington sends dispatch to Colonel Samuel Griffin, to immediately transport his Philadelphia regiment across the Delaware River, south of Burlington, and move toward high ground near Mount Holly, New Jersey. Colonel Griffin's regiment is filled with boys and older men but will be supported by the South Jersey militia. The general has also directed his adjutant, Joseph Reed, to escort a small number of light artillery pieces across the river, meeting up with Griffin's forces near Mount Holly. Meanwhile, Hamilton sends word to Betsy Ross, who is well acquainted with Reed, to ferry from Philadelphia to New Jersey and meet him no later than winter's first day. Reed has been ordered to "set the table" for the count, but he does not know Betsy is the honey pot. In fact, only Hamilton's team and the Congressional "flag" committee are aware of Betsy's status as a Continental Army agent.

The mission to draw Colonel von Donop's brigades south, and detain him with distraction, is top secret and more important than Betsy's potential exposure. Moriah has been ordered to split up with Ephraim, prior to Bordentown, making her way back to Washington's command to provide intelligence on Hessian forces and disposition prior to the attack on Trenton.

Ephraim will try to attach himself to the Hessian and Scottish units as they move south to counter the exaggerated threat from Colonel Griffin. At which point, his primary mission will be Betsy's success and to guard her life. Hamilton harbors doubt about Joseph Reed's loyalty to Washington, if not the American cause. As a connected Philadelphia lawyer, Hamilton suspects Reed may have knowledge of the count's land maneuvers in Bucks County. Hamilton has instructed Washington to inform Reed that he will know the female agent meeting him in New Jersey by the code word, "Fidelia." General Washington agrees to inform Captain Hamilton immediately, if Reed reacts to this word, though the general finds the request odd. Hamilton takes additional precautions as well.

By Saturday, December 21, Griffin's forces have fortified a hilltop on the south side of Rancocas Creek in view of the village of Mount Holly to the north. The 42nd Highlanders, the famed Black Watch, attached to Colonel von Donop's command are stationed at outposts between Mount Holly and Bordentown. While Joseph Reed arrives with cannon, strengthening the hill fortifications, Continental units probe miles north of Mount Holly and bloody the Scots, again led by Colonel Thomas Stirling. Stirling informs the count, who dispatches a local and clear "loyal subject of the crown," one Ephraim Johns, who has recently supplied his brigades with much needed fodder. He is to reconnoiter the town and quickly report back as to the rebel strength and position.

Colonel Thomas Stirling independently moves a battalion of the 42nd south toward Mount Holly, as his most southerly units report being taken under surprise by mere schoolboys. He has recommended that Colonel von Donop move the remainder of the brigade toward Mount Holly, for he believes they can quickly rout the Americans. Ephraim slips south, prior to the highlanders reaching the outskirts of the town. He plans to enter the town alone and find Fidelia.

Earlier, Betsy Ross has found Joseph Reed, who is preparing the empty home of a deceased physician, Doctor van Ridder, who died the previous winter of smallpox. The home is suitable to her purpose and Reed explains the military action is a ruse, a simple diversionary assault designed to pull Colonel von Donop's forces out of position. Betsy is tasked to find a way to detain the count until after Christmas. The town's mayor has supplied Reed with a list of royal supporters, and Reed has arranged for the families to be detained and escorted back to Philadelphia. Betsy will be known as the widow Febe van Ridder and can only hope the few remaining townsfolk, and she, can keep her cover until the day following Christmas.

Ephraim arrives in the village and is quickly spotted by Betsy. Musket volleys are heard to the north, and a hurried plan forms in Betsy's mind. Ephraim believes the highlanders will not move on the town without the count, and that Colonel von Donop will move cautiously until he reports back. Betsy knows the timing is uncertain. She begins ransacking the house and tells Ephraim not to touch the beds, tables or chairs. The silver must be stolen. Betsy rushes out on the front lawn, hails middle-aged riflemen, some of the few Pennsylvania regulars under Griffin's command, and tells them to take the "Tory silver." The soldiers express mild shock, and Betsy can only hope she isn't recognized. She thinks it a small matter, as the current mission will likely be her last performance. Now she must tell Ephraim the most critical portion of her plan, and she knows not whom it will pain more.

Ephraim immediately protests, as Betsy explains she must return with him to Colonel von Donop's command. Betsy assures Ephraim, "I must meet the count on his ground, as a Tory refugee, escaping arrest or worse at the hands of Colonel Griffin's forces." Ephraim retorts, "You may be recognized," but both realize the risk is moot. "No," replies Betsy, "My plan may work, but you must appear seriously injured." Before Ephraim can again protest, Betsy states, "I believe the injury will cause you less distress than what I also must have you do." Ephraim is not often speechless, but he remains quiet, for he knows what Betsy is thinking. Betsy continues, "You will need to cleanly break my left arm." Ephraim would rather face a galley full of murderous pirates, as he listens to Betsy explain, "The injury will be slight compared to what I may face with no weapon to appeal to the count's common humility." Ephraim hands her his loaded pistol and directs Betsy graze his left arm with the lead ball. As the black powder smoke fills his face, Ephraim turns and smashes his forehead on a mantle, referring the pain of the wound. He shouts for Betsy to place her arm over two leaves of a table, and he quickly snaps the arm clean. Luckily, she passes out immediately, and Ephraim dresses their wounds for travel.

CHAPTER FIVE

SCENE 1

Victory or Death

Preparation for Battle • South Jersey and Bucks County • late December 1776

BY THE MORNING OF DECEMBER 23, 1776, Colonel von Donop's Hessian regiments and artillery have moved more than ten miles south in full support of the 42nd Highlanders. While the Royal forces, thousands strong, force Colonel Griffin's battalions to retreat south of Mount Holly to the fortified hills overlooking the Rancocas Creek, Ephraim heads back north, east of the fighting, and works his way to the rear of the Hessian lines. In rudimentary Dutch-German, Ephraim convinces a Hessian officer that Betsy, who is in and out of consciousness due the pain of jarring travel, is an injured loyalist whom he has rescued and who requires immediate medical attention.

Colonel von Donop is unimpressed with the quality of the rebel forces facing him. Skirmishes make clear the enemy is mostly boys, supported by militia and sharpshooters. Anticipating the current level of intelligence, Ephraim does not overplay his hand with the colonel. Yet the story of the young women immediately intrigues the count, more so since a Hessian officer has described Betsy as exceedingly fair. Count von Donop instructs the officer to bid his private physician attend the woman. Ephraim explains the town is lightly fortified and mostly deserted, as loyalists have been arrested and worse in Betsy's case. He describes hearing Betsy, the widow van Ridder, crying for help, as militia attempt to abuse her inside her own home. Realizing the scene, the count simply states, "A buccaneer's life may strengthen a man's resolve," referring to Ephraim's past, and he takes a mental note that Ephraim may be another man who can further his endeavors in Bucks County.

Betsy Ross awakens, lying in a medical field tent, to the faces of strange men but one. Ephraim quickly, but gently, states, "Febe, this is the Count von Donop, our king's servant. You are in safe hands." Betsy winces as a pain throbs in her left arm. She remains light-headed and feels a throbbing of her forehead as well. Either her head has been bruised in travel or Ephraim has "dutifully" enhanced her disguise. Colonel von Donop smoothly states in German, "Madam, we shall restore your health, and then we shall endeavor to restore your home." Betsy, with pursed full lips, can only respond with a partially audible *"Danke schön"* before fading unconscious.

The same afternoon, less than thirty miles away as the crow flies, General Washington is fully in preparation for one of history's great Hail Mary throws. A few thousand troops have arrived late from their escape through western Jersey, and some regular troops have agreed to stay in the fight seeing the zeal of Pennsylvania and New Jersey militia. Peer pressure can be a powerful tool for a desperate commander, and Washington does not deign to lecture his common soldiers on the eve of battle. Instead, he employs the words of his friend, Thomas Paine, the son of an English sharecropper and common tradesman, who is a well-known patriot pamphleteer and a "Philosopher of Freedom." Paine has written "Crisis," specifically to bolster morale and support for the attack on Trenton. Washington has the piece read aloud to his soldiers:

> *These are the times that try men's souls. The summer soldier and the*
> *sunshine patriot will, in this crisis, shrink from the service of their*
> *country; but he that stands by now deserves the love and thanks*
> *of man and woman. Tyranny, like hell, is not easily conquered;*
> *yet we have this consolation with us, that the*
> *harder the conflict, the more glorious the triumph [...]*

In ironic twist, Paine will become a future resident of Bordentown and Carl von Donop, in the much nearer future, will wish he had remained so.

Back in Jersey, Ephraim Johns outlines colonial artillery positions on the hills south of Mount Holly. Artillery on the hills, as well as the natural moat provided by the Rancocas Creek, will allow continued rebel threat to the town. Colonel von Donop, already suffering confirmation bias brought on by the sight of the widow van Ridder, is determined to rid the area of rebel threat. Curious, Ephraim thinks, none of the Hessian senior officers challenge the tactical wisdom of the count's course of action, while the Scots desire no more than to scatter a militia that has continually threatened their most exposed southern encampments.

SCENE 2

Widow's Reprisal

Mount Holly • South Jersey • Christmas Eve 1776

By evening on December 23, Colonel von Donop's forces have secured the village of Mount Holly. Carl's mind is preoccupied. He has ordered Febe van Ridder's house restored as best possible and makes her home his headquarters. As Betsy recovers, asleep in a downstairs bedroom, sporadic musket and cannon fire are heard in the distance. The count is annoyed by the cannon fire, although he believes the rebels well out of range of the widow's home, since the disturbance meant to taunt the Hessians will only disrupt his guest's recovery.

The following morning, Christmas Eve, Betsy wakes to the harsh sound of competing cannonades. Neither the Hessian nor the American gunners can reach the other, and have effectuated a stalemate, as either can pin down opposing infantry on opposite sides of the creek. Hessian commanders quickly determine Colonel Griffin may easily retreat, will not attack, and they advise Colonel von Donop to retire at least one heavy grenadier infantry brigade back to Bordentown. In Bordentown, the brigades may support either Colonel Rahl in Trenton or the count's position to the south.

Count von Donop will not be moved, and he will not strip himself of superior force deep in New Jersey without adequate cavalry reconnaissance. He believes a Virginian army could come up the Mullica River to Burr's Mill, threaten his position from the east, and he will not hear word of it until they arrive for a morning feast. Food is on the count's mind. He means to break his guest's fast and has a noon meal prepared for a stirring Febe van Ridder. As the afternoon sun dips in the sky, the Hessian infantry grows restless. A grenadier sergeant in the Linsing regiment approaches a *jäger* captain, Johann Ewald, about the delay in their movement. Ewald replies with sarcasm that the count is busy *spielen Haus* with the injured woman.

On Christmas Day, Washington's forces are back on the move in Bucks County. Robert Robersen, near Yardley, sends word to Moses Doan, a hard ride twenty miles north at the gang's hideout in the high rocks above the Tohickon Creek. A thousand troops or more, supported by artillery, have moved south of Yardley, headed for Morrisville, where they can cross the river and threaten both Trenton and Bordentown. More threatening is news that the remaining Continental Army, possibly three thousand strong, is gathering at McConkey's Ferry.

Both Moses and Robersen are aware that hundreds of Durham Boats, large specialized river transports made to carry iron to Philadelphia port, have been collecting down river from the Durham Ironworks. Each boat can transport an infantry company, or artillery and horses. Taken as a whole, and given the current position of Hessian forces, Robersen notifies Moses what he already suspects. General Washington is throwing everything he has at Trenton, possibly in a double envelopment, and utilizing artillery the Americans may enfilade the forming German lines from across the river in Morrisville.

Robersen's letter continues, "I will speak plainly, these circumstances threaten our business, and I mean to hold you to your cousin's bargain of fifty guineas for our previous engagement." Moses is not a man to head threats, his cousin less so, however, this is a statement of fact, a reminder of a business contract. In spite of this fact, the Doan gang is spending their income as fast as it arrives, and Moses turns his mind to the matter at hand. The rebels hold nearly all the ferry crossings. He will be forced to go north to cross the Delaware River unsuspected. Riding hard, he will be pained to make Trenton before midnight. Looking to Abraham, Moses states, "Cousin, we are against a wall and pray may it not place our heads in the noose." Moses will travel alone, and with an extra horse, to alert Colonel Rahl in Trenton. He sends Abraham and Jacob overland to try and reach Bristol, thence Bordentown, well before sunrise.

The Doan face the same obstacles as American Continental forces. While not frozen over, the Delaware River is choked with ice and bitter cold winds slow travel. For many of General Washington's troops, some shod in rags for shoes, the weather will be deadlier than Hessian iron. Although American artillery takes up position across from Trenton that night, none of the soldiers sent southeast crosses the river. Washington's historic crossing, again effectuated by soldier mariners from Massachusetts, does not provide him the full advantage he hoped. Rahl's fifteen hundred professionals will face twenty-four hundred Americans, but Washington cannot yet know the success of Betsy's ruse.

Back in Jersey, Carl von Donop is clearly smitten by the understated charms of the widow van Ridder. Betsy's display of easy charm and gratitude, with little hint of overawe to the count's nobility, has completely won his affection. To meet such a beautiful and intelligent woman, a Dutch-German woman no less, on the eve of his most favored holiday, when surely he should feel the melancholy of a lack of family, and to be nestled in a quaint frontier province on a snowy Christmas night. Such perfection prevents any suspicion of espionage, "Wizardry indeed," thinks Betsy, and the count freely abandons the duties of his rank.

After a fine diner eaten with silver service requisitioned from the major, the count begins telling stories of Paris and Moscow. Offering his guest wine brought from Europe, Betsy could not help but feel the effects of the alcohol. The count, far more accustomed to strong wine than she, begins drawing himself closer and while logs crackle on the fire asks to kiss Betsy. Being coy, she responds, "Is it not too early for a *guten Abend kiss?*" The count simply smiles. Betsy explains that she feels perfectly comfortable with him, and yet is in real pain that the wine has only partially helped mask. Quoting Martin Luther, the count states, *"Wein kommt von Gott,"* and bids Betsy drink more. As the clock approaches midnight, Betsy gambles. She entreats for the count to forestall his affections until her arm has healed, kissing him lightly on the cheek. Thanking him for his care and affection, Betsy takes leave to retire to bed alone. Carl Emil Ulrich von Donop is in no rush, he feels time is on his side, yet within hours his world will come crashing down.

SCENE 3

Irony of Defeat

Battle of Trenton • New Jersey • December 26, 1776

Before noon after Christmas, Johann Rahl lay bleeding in the snow. His life wanes in the coming hours and with it a culture he protected yet did not fully enjoy. Within their high columned walls and warm rooms filled with Oriental rugs, Flemish tapestries and Dutch paintings, the European continental nobility, an ocean away, hears no noise nor the flutter of wind, yet a spirit moves and an invisible crack opens in their walls.

Washington's crossing lies nine miles northwest of the Hessian camp in Trenton. The American forces split up, with General John Sullivan leading the vanguard along the river toward Trenton. Forces under Nathanael Greene take the longer northeast route into town, thereby preventing Hessian forward units from alerting British forces at Pennington or retreating northeast. Alexander Hamilton's New York artillery travels with the northern division and once within the town will help close off an avenue to retreat with canister shot. The plan is to hit hard in a predawn attack, but the weather delays the Americans by hours, and it is light when Washington's forces approach the town. A large Pennsylvania militia company independently attacks Hessian forward units in the dark of night, and Washington, livid with its leader, dresses him down, stating, "You sir, may have ruined all my plans by having them put on their guard."

Yet Colonel Rahl is relieved, not alerted, thinking the minor skirmish is all he may expect that morning. Heavy cannon fire, from across the river, will dissuade him of any such idea. By the time Colonel Rahl exits his headquarters, his three grenadier regiments are forming up on South King and Queen Streets. The Americans have already scattered his smaller forward units, and all five major roads out of town, including the bridge over the creek toward Bordentown, are cut off. For Rahl, insult and injury swiftly follow.

King and Queen streets in Trenton come to a pointed intersection, a crown if you will, from south to north. Rahl's engineers and officers advised he build a fortified redoubt at the head of this crown, defending roads radiating northeast to Princeton and northwest to Pennington. The colonel ignored the advice, essentially daring an attack, and fate hands him all he deserves. With Sullivan behind him on the river and cannon fire strafing along his lines from behind, Rahl has no choice but to form up his regiments and march up King-Queen streets to the peak of the crown, where Washington waits with cannon and musket. Rahl and his troops fight bravely, but the Americans know they have him and press their advantage. Colonel Rahl and nearly every senior Hessian officer is killed or wounded, as the remaining officers seek terms of surrender.

The Trenton victory seems small in absolute numbers in a time when Americans speak in billions and trillions, but the impact is global. Highly experienced infantry regiments, some of Europe's finest, are destroyed. Nearly a thousand Hessians are sent to prison in Lancaster, to be guarded by the sons of Pennsylvania Dutch who fled central Europe, including Germany, in the previous decades. The British king will have to compensate his uncle for the loss of every man, and the opportunity cost of this manpower is felt in the coming days, let alone years. Most important, the Americans capture cannon, thousands of muskets, rifles and ammunition, as well as boots and food, including the salted meats!

The victory allows Washington to once again outfox the British generals hurried to Trenton to confront the threat a week latter. Invigorated, the Americans avoid a large force under Lord Cornwallis, again withdrawing under cover of darkness, and smash the large British garrison at Princeton. Both sides retire for winter, with Cornwallis canceling his return to England, likely not wanting to prostrate himself before his king and explain how fortune has favored the bold Washington.

His majesty, King George III, has no intention of giving up his sovereign rights to an entire continental seaboard, and the conflict will drag on for another five years. Yet the odds have shifted. Victory has strengthened the American cause. Washington gained valuable experience and will continue to utilize strategic geographic depth, like a Russian. The general simply must avoid being cornered, and in little more than a year, Ben Franklin, America's first superstar, and supporters such as the Marquis de Lafayette will utilize this newly won vigor to convince the French Kingdom to enter the war against her ancient rival. The war will bankrupt both great kingdoms and leave a United States the sovereign of her own land, a wealth in new lands that will one day outweigh the old world's gold more a thousand times a thousand.

SCENE 4

Pistols Fore Noon

Burlington Ferry • New Jersey • December 26, 1776

Moses can only watch as he stands near the rebel batteries pounding Trenton from Morrisville, Pennsylvania. Since early morning he has been twice shot at, once outracing militia and a second time by Hessian pickets near the Princeton Pike. "My effort was for naught," he mumbles to himself. "Colonel Rahl dismissed me roughly," showing suspicion for a man in the employ of the count, thinks Moses out loud. Clearly, Rahl has informants of his own in Colonel von Donop's regiments. Moses is truly lucky he was not treated to some enhanced interrogation given suspicions surrounding the massacre in Hunterdon. Exasperated, Moses continues mumbling, "I even left a note with Colonel Rahl's adjutant, warning of the pending attack." *No matter now*, thinks Moses, *Rahl's war is finished!* By mid-afternoon, Moses' real concern is for his cousin. Abraham and Jacob are to meet him in Morrisville, and they are overdue.

Previously arriving in Bristol, the morning after Christmas, Jacob and Abraham are apprised of the fighting around Mont Holly by drunkards homeward bound from the King George Inn. Not wanting to alert the ferrymen with enquiry, the two decide to split up in Burlington, New Jersey. Abraham will head south for Mount Holly, while Jacob travels north for Bordentown.

Prior to sunrise, Ephraim Johns is worried. He has kept close to the van Ridder house during the night and has no indication Betsy is endangered. Yet he can wait no longer. The Hessian garrison at Trenton may already be under attack, he thinks, and dispatch riders may be speeding toward Mount Holly. Betsy's cover will certainly not hold until her arm heals, and the count may be a changed man on receiving news of a defeat. Hiding in a holly bush, behind the home, and watching the darkened room where Betsy sleeps, Ephraim makes his move. He catches the rear sentinel off guard and takes the man silently from behind. Knocking firmly on a window rouses Betsy from a nervous sleep. He bids her grab her warm hooded cape, boots and a gown, pulling her out the window without responding to argument. They must move quickly before the count discovers she is gone. Ephraim has no choice

Chapter Five   61

but to guide Betsy through unbeaten path until they can clear the western pickets of the town.

In half an hour, before the sun rises in the east, the pair steals a horse and head northwest on the Burlington Road. As the horizon behind begins to lighten, Ephraim can make out a rider speedily traveling toward him. Word of the battle surely, he thinks. As the rider passes, Ephraim nods, holding Betsy close to his chest. She is bowed and partially asleep, but the hood of the cape is back against the knot of her hair and the rider, Abraham Doan, takes the scene in double as he gallops past. Abraham recognizes the face, but he cannot stop and does not believe his eyes.

Well before eight in the morning, a nervous grenadier hustles Abraham into the van Ridder home. The count is not dressed for an audience and barks at two *jäger* to locate the woman if she is not in *dem Scheißhaus!* The sight of Abraham changes his countenance from disturbed to quizzical, abruptly. The count shouts, staring, *"Warum bist du hier?"* Abraham calmly states, "Trenton is assaulted." Switching to English, the count asks by whom, and Abraham responds, "The entire rebel army." Colonel von Donop's arms slacken. He has been run through yet feels no pain. The count's unconscious mind has immediately grasped what he will know in the coming seconds.

A jäger enters the room, exclaiming he can find neither the widow nor the African man. The count is unmoved and does not respond, but Abraham looks directly at him and states, "I saw them together headed for Burlington." Colonel von Donop shoos Abraham with a slight wave of the hand, saying merely, "They are spies."

Within a few minutes, Abraham and a pair of dragoons are riding hard for the western Hessian pickets. He hopes to catch the two spies before they reach the river. Abraham swaps horses near Burr's road with a cavalry officer, and he dearly purchases the man's loaded pistol. Hoping rebel militia won't stop him before he reaches Burlington, Abraham spurs his horse the final seven miles. Ephraim and Betsy are being pulled and rowed back to Bristol when Abraham arrives at the ferry dock. Traffic is light, and he provides the operator with a gold guinea to have the strongest men quickly ferry him across the river. Abraham further bribes the rowers, halfway across, and they can only speculate as to the reason for their strained effort. The quarry is in sight, however, and Abraham can eye the pair as they debark their ferry.

Ephraim does not need to speculate, as his ferry team is shocked that the operator's brothers lean into oars at regatta pace rather than drink Christmas beer on the Jersey bank. A single man worries Ephraim. He recognizes the rider from earlier and knows he's von Donop's man. Colonel von Donop can afford a professional man hunter, and Ephraim asks Betsy if she recognizes their pursuer. "Maybe," she responds, "But if it is the Doan I expect, we will not outrun him." Ephraim determines to stand his ground and bids Betsy find help.

"Curious," thinks Abraham out loud. He hoped to chase the pair down on lonely roads. The black man is larger than he. And the face, the face he saw was of a man who knew pain, "Yet more pain will come," he whispers. Abraham checks the pistol he purchased, thrusting it in a waist belt. He then cocks and primes his own pistol, preparing to fire as the ferry approaches the ramp. Ephraim is ready. He'll have one shot, as his damaged left arm will hamper handling a second pistol. He pulls from his boot a razor sharp Wharncliffe blade, a "murder" knife with long worn Baleen handle scales. Boarding ships at sea, the knife has often been his last line of defense. Ephraim quickly secures the sheathed knife to his left side belt.

Abraham's left-hand rests on the tomahawk nestled against his hip. Before the ferry strikes wood, he fires, shattering Ephraim's left clavicle, and immediately dips down to a knee as Ephraim's pained shot ricochets off the rising boat's brow, hitting a ferryman behind. Abraham instinctively stands, pulling the second pistol, but as Ephraim comes forward at speed the pistol misfires and Abraham is forced to roll as Ephraim comes down upon him from the brow. Ephraim is in his natural element, but Abraham's strength and speed allow him to grasp the shoulder wound. Ephraim loses grip on the knife, and Abraham kicks the blade away while pulling out the tomahawk.

Rifled shots ring out before Abraham can deliver the *coup de grâce*. He turns around to see two colonial riflemen, Bristol sentinels, approaching the docks with Betsy. Abraham immediately sheaths the tomahawk and runs off the back of the ferry, jumping into the first ferry as it moves past in desperation. His landing provides the craft extra momentum toward Burlington, facilitating an escape.

In haste, Betsy tries to apply a gentle pressure on Ephraim's bleeding shoulder with a torn length of her gown. She pleads for the soldiers to help him into town and attempts to run and find a doctor, but Ephraim has her wrist and pulls her to ear, saying, "He knows your face, I'm sorry I couldn't kill him." Betsy takes his hand in both of hers and tells him softly, "Don't worry dear Ephraim, Abraham Doan has placed the noose around his own neck."

CHAPTER SIX

SCENE 1

The Ring

Morristown, North Jersey • early February 1777

SECURE IN WINTER ENCAMPMENT in northern Jersey, George Washington is well pleased with his newly appointed aide-de-camp, Lt. Colonel Alexander Hamilton. The Colonel has unfinished business, however, and provides Moriah Strong a confidential letter to be delivered to Colonel von Donop as follows:

My Lord,

I have of most recent been appointed personal aide to his Excellency, General George Washington. As staff officer, I have relinquished all previous duties and call upon your good nature and honor to forgive all trespass and injury due my servants in the dispatch of their duties in honor of their countrymen. I have only supposition as to my Lord's appraisal with the identity of the known agent, a woman fidelia, who has been guest of your hospitality this Christmas past. As I have freed my collaborators of further martial duty, it is my ardent hope that you will free your contemplation of reprisal in their regard. With all respect and honor, your servant,

Colonel Alexander Hamilton.

The count receives the letter within the week and reads the contents carefully. Moses has previously informed him of Betsy's identity, and he has in turn instructed the Doan to avoid molesting her in any fashion. The black man is a separate matter, his identity and whereabouts are yet undetermined. Carl von Donop knew well the veiled threat behind the letter. Someone in Philadelphia has not been sufficiently compensated for discretion or else Lord

Stirling has chosen honor over family interest. The latter is of concern, since a man of means can reach out beyond oceans. No matter, thinks the count, he will find his African friend, as he will be least missed. Of greater concern, his plans for Bucks County are compromised. The count may require straw men to continue acquiring rights to properties, and the British must prevail in the conflict or all his work and expenditure is surely wasted.

By early June 1777, the widow Elizabeth Phoebe Ross née Griscom, known to her friends as Betsy, has put behind thoughts of Christmas. With a newly won confidence in the air, Betsy finds springtime love and will marry the patriot sailor Joseph Ashburn within the coming weeks. Joseph agrees to allow Betsy to repurpose the wedding ring John Ross had given her. Betsy has Joseph's name inscribed inside the ring, opposite John's, and as she wished, the goldsmith adorns the ring with detail of his own design. Inside the ring the smith has etched thirteen stars in constellation with the names of her loves, and a thought enters her mind.

The flag attributed to Betsy, the Quaker daughter of families who immigrated to the Delaware Valley nearly a hundred years prior, is a symbol of unity and a symbol of natural freedom. The sacrifices made by colonial Americans are great during the war, but sacrifice has long been part of life. Betsy Ross is a middle child of seventeen siblings, and few survive childhood. Betsy, as many Americans, has an instinct for unity, for family, and a constellation of stars has great appeal.

Fittingly, in late summer 1777, while encamped near the Little Neshaminy Creek in Bucks County, Washington receives a new arrival to North America. A nineteen-year-old French noble, the Marquis de Lafayette, bows before the general. The young idealist, a disciple of Enlightenment, had joined the French army at thirteen and was married and the inheritor of two great family fortunes before sixteen. Against the wishes of his king, Lafayette offers Washington his enthusiastic military service and influence in helping Benjamin Franklin move France toward recognizing the independence of the United States and joining the war in alliance against Great Britain. Lafayette brings gifts for the general from across the sea, but a special gift is acquired much closer. At the advice of Ben Franklin, Lafayette has inquired as to the flag of the new nation. Congress presents him with the Stars and Stripes in constellation, a new flag sewn by Betsy Ross Ashburn.

For Our Freedom and Yours

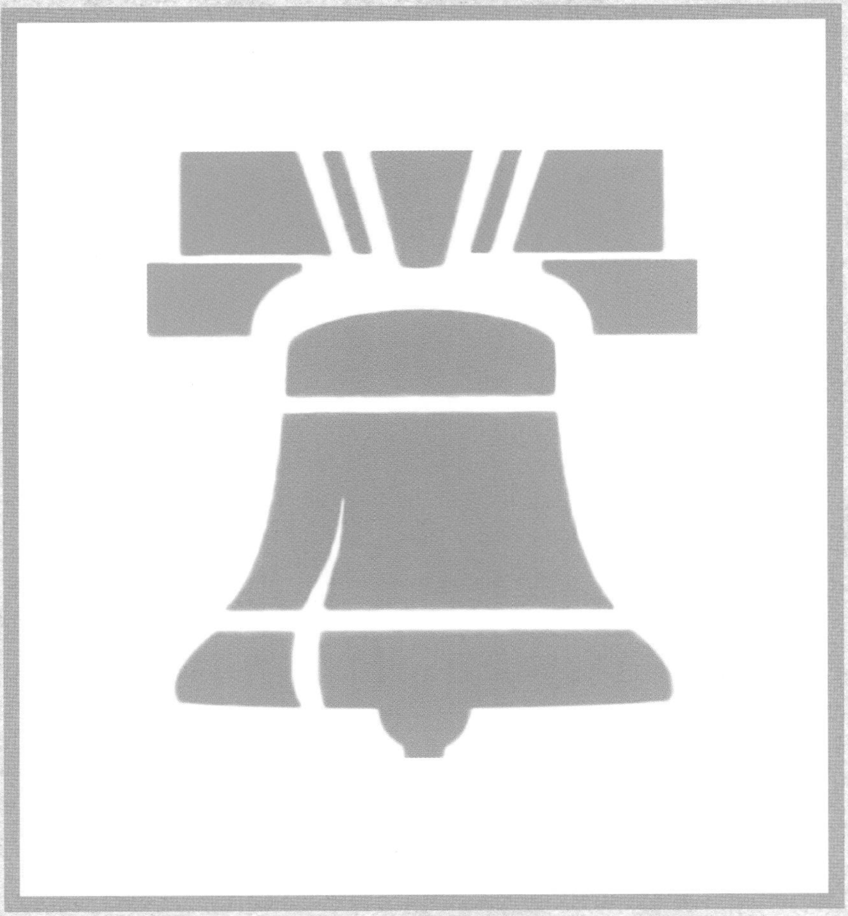

SCENE 2

Lost the Plot

Hartsville, Bucks County, Pennsylvania • August 1777

The young Lafayette is honored with the title Major General of the American Continental Army. He joins the council of war held by Washington's major generals at the Moland House headquarters in mid August 1777. Marching north for Jersey, earlier in the month, Washington receives word from Congress that the entire British fleet is spotted heading south off Cape May. Washington is unaware of General Howe's true intentions. He simply stops the army in place, near water of the Little Neshaminy Creek, at the intersection of Old York and Bristol Roads. While encamped, another nobleman, the thirty-two-year-old Count Casimir Pulaski joins Washington's army. Casimir fled the Polish and Lithuanian Commonwealth following a failed attempt to free his homeland from Russian imperial domination.

Casimir becomes a Brigadier General and a "Father" of the American Cavalry Corps. He gives his life in battle a few years later at Savannah, Georgia. Near the county seat of Bucks County, only a short ride from the Moland House, is a memorial to the fighting spirit of Poland. The great winged Hussar memorializes Poles who died fighting German Nazi domination. A dominion thwarted by the United States, the nation Casimir, a great Hussar, helped give life.

British General John Burgoyne attacked south from Canada, via Lake Champlain, earlier in the summer of 1777 and recaptured Fort Ticonderoga. This northern British army, including Hessian and Indian allies, numbered near eight thousand strong and directly threatens Albany, the greater Hudson Valley and the entirety of New England. In fact, the British plan seems for Howe to bring the main British army up the Hudson Valley, join with Burgoyne, and cut off Boston and New England from the rest of the colonies. This exact strategy terrified Washington's New England Major Generals, Greene and Putnam, the previous year. Howe commanded near twenty thousand soldiers and marines around New York. He could easily have stolen a march on Washington, near Philadelphia in early August, and moved a royal force up the Hudson Valley to link up with his subordinate, General Burgoyne.

A chokehold on New England, with a naval blockade of Boston, may have forced Washington's hand. Howe has been unsuccessfully trying to force the American army into one decisive battle all spring, and it occurs to George Washington that Howe has lost the plot. Washington knows he can't help the southern city of Charleston, South Carolina, if it is the British fleet's target. He simply stays put, and sets up headquarters at the widow Moland's house, awaiting additional news of Howe's movement.

Unsupported by the Howe brothers, General Burgoyne's northern British army is bogged down in the wilds of upstate New York and is sequentially defeated by a quickly growing patriot army of the north. The American's, under General Gates, force Burgoyne to surrender his entire army on October 17, 1777 following a second engagement near Saratoga.

Less than sixteen weeks later, once word of the British surrender at the second Battle of Saratoga reaches the French King across the sea, Benjamin Franklin and King Louis XVI sign a Treaty of Alliance on February 6, 1778. The treaty binds the United States and France in opposition against Great Britain. King George subsequently declares war on France five weeks later, sealing his own eventual defeat and forcing Britain to recognize the independence of the United States of America with the signing of the Treaty of Paris on September 3, 1783. This final resolution comes more than two years after the surrender of General Lord Cornwallis at the final major battle of the war at Yorktown, Virginia, in October of 1781.

General William Howe and his brother, Admiral Lord Richard Howe, hold wide command latitude given the communication difficulties between America and London. We cannot fully know the motives and thinking of the Howe brothers. We do know they land more than fifteen thousand men up the Elk River, in Maryland, and march their army for Philadelphia, aiming to cut off the head of the snake, the rebellious Congress. The colonial government, the Continental Congress, will simply retire west toward Lancaster and thence York, Pennsylvania, by mid September 1777.

A theory on the movement of the Howe brothers that summer may tie back to the death of their eldest brother, George Augustus Howe, 3rd Viscount Howe, who died fighting in the French and Indian war in 1758. Then prime minister, William Pitt, wanted to make George the commander of British Forces in the colony, but not yet thirty-two he was made Brig. General under

an older man's command. Again, near Fort Ticonderoga, George Howe is killed fighting valiantly and dies in the arms of Israel Putnam. Putnam, Washington's future Major General, and the men of Massachusetts are so taken with the leadership of the dashing Howe, who slept on the ground with them and led from the front in battle, they commission a Westminster monument in his honor. George Howe was a family light, a star, and was likely idolized by his younger brothers. He is also the only peer of the British realm to be interred in America. George was buried at Albany, New York. The thought of taking the city by fire and sword, thence marching east in a Sherman like slaughter of the men whose fathers so loved and honored their brother may well have weighted heavy on both men. Lord Richard Howe, a good friend of Benjamin

Franklin, and his younger brother William may have thought such a campaign a bridge too far. If so, history has proven the wisdom of their judgment, as the destruction necessitated by such a march may have prevented the two great allies from their collaborations in the pivotal twentieth century.

Whatever their motives, General William Howe and his Hessian allies are again tactically proficient. They engage the equivalently sized American Continental Army confronting them south of Philadelphia on September 11, 1777 at Chadds Ford. The Germans again hold the American center stationary, as Howe crosses the Brandywine Creek out of range of poor colonial reconnaissance and directly attacks Washington's right flank. Following a grueling daylong battle in which Washington is once again lucky to retreat with his life, the Americans flee north, and the British triumphantly enter Philadelphia on September 26 to an empty Independence Hall.

SCENE 3

Absolution Lost

The Delaware River, Philadelphia and South Jersey • October 1777

Following the Battle at Brandywine, Carl von Donop knows he's deep in the shadow of his new commander, the fêted Prussian General Wilhelm Knyphausen. The Colonel seeks opportunity for absolution due the taint of Trenton and a return to battlefield glory. On October 4, a large American army assaults Howe's forces encamped at Germantown on Philadelphia's outskirts. The surprise attack devolves in confusion, and the Americans are repulsed. Nevertheless, having been caught off guard and with fewer troops, General Howe recombines his entire army back within central Philadelphia, endeavoring to defeat the American river fortifications preventing his reinforcement via the Delaware River. As General Washington prepares to retire his army for winter at Valley Forge, Colonel von Donop perceives an opportunity to reclaim his honor and keep his new world ambitions on track.

The Continental Congress has provided for strong defenses of the Delaware River below Philadelphia. Mud Island lies south of the Delaware and Schuylkill River confluence, within the modern Philadelphia city limits.

Fort Mifflin is located on the island and across the river, on high ground at Red Bank, New Jersey, stands Fort Mercer. Spanning the river in front of the forts, the Pennsylvania Navy set down rows of sunken chevaux-de-frise, essentially great wooden boxes filled with large rocks and anchored to the riverbed such that passing ships may be impaled on large, angled, metal tipped poles reaching to just below the waterline. The American Continental Navy and the Pennsylvania Navy have large numbers of floating artillery barges, fire ships, artillery row galleys and smaller gunned warships ready to destroy larger entrapped British ships.

For the British, however, the clear military objective is to attack upriver, keeping the American Navies occupied, while assaulting Fort Mercer with land-based forces crossing to the north from Philadelphia to Camden. Colonel von Donop offers the service of his regiments to General Howe for a direct assault on Fort Mercer. Howe desperately needs to open the Delaware River for the supply and comfort of his army bottled up in Philadelphia for the harsh winter to come.

An urgent note arrives in Plumstead, Bucks County, for Moses Doan. Count von Donop requires his immediate service, providing intelligence on militia activity at Fort Mercer and the Jersey communities surrounding. Neither Moses nor Abraham is available, as both are following a lead on Ephraim Johns in the Trenton area. Traveling the Easton road to Philadelphia will take most of a day, and Mahlon Doan makes an executive decision. Mahlon and Jacob will perform the task requested by the count.

George Washington knows Fort Mercer will be attacked. He sends the French engineer, Thomas-Antoine du Plessis, to improve the defenses of the fort. The defense is steep mud embankment, finished with a high palisade wall of sharpened tree trunks that rise from the top of the embankment at near forty-five degrees. The trees are cut down from the surrounding orchards of James Whitall's Red Bank farm. Congress offered to purchase the property earlier in 1777. However, Whitall claims his Quaker faith prevents him from favoring either side in a military conflict. A portion of his property is seized and utilized by the army without his consent.

Thomas du Plessis immediately recognizes the New Jersey militia has constructed too large a fort for the given ground and the number of men who will defend her. The north end of the fort is closer to the woods and du Plessis has an interior wall built, cutting the fort's size by more than half. This creates a stockade, which is cleared as a killing box for interior stationed cannon and riflemen. Unfortunate souls who scale the outer north wall find themselves trapped, impinged by obstacles, and are quickly cut down by canister shot and musket balls. On the riverside, past the beach, the ground rises steeply by thirty feet before the walls of the fort are raised. Even so, the British will not easily breach the river fortifications to land marines on the beach in support of the Hessian infantry. The southern ground in front of the fort, and to its east, is open and provides the defenders with a killing field up to three hundred paces.

In a prescient move, General Washington decides to replace the defending force of Fort Mercer. He supplants the New Jersey militia with regular army units of the 1st and 2nd Rhode Island, under Colonel Christopher Greene. A relative of Major General Nathanael Greene, Colonel Greene commands units with a fierce fighting reputation. His units are unique in that they contain a high percentage of former slaves, American Indians, and free Black Americans.

With odds stacked against them, these American soldiers will inflict the highest mortality rate the Germans receive throughout the revolution. On Wednesday, October 22, very late in the afternoon, as many as two thousand Hessians prepare to assault Fort Mercer. Roughly four hundred men defend the fort, mostly members of the Rhode Island regiments. In less than one hour nearly a third of the Hessian soldiers are turned into casualties. Hundreds will be left dead and dying below the walls and in the fields surrounding the fort. Many casualties are simply left on the road during the long retreat toward Haddonfield. The Jersey militia is unavailable to maul the beleaguered retreating soldiers, and the lost opportunity may have prevented a great victory from becoming an infamous slaughter.

The loss of life helps line the pockets of the Hessian Prince Frederick, as his nephew, King George, will again compensate him in gold for every man lost. History does not make claim as to how well the grieving German families are themselves compensated. European shock, with the lopsided victory, will help push the French to increase military support of the American revolutionary cause and its pugnacious adherents. The support seals the fate of British imperial rule in the united American colonies.

SCENE 4

Road to Redemption

Near Woodbury, South Jersey • October 19 – 22, 1777

By Sunday evening, October 19, 1777, Mahlon Doan and Jacob arrive in Haddonfield, New Jersey, ahead of Colonel von Donop's Hessian army and begin to gather intelligence near the Indian King Tavern. They hear regular army units have moved through the area in the previous days, and the town is buzzing with talk of African soldiers defending Fort Mercer. Clearly, this is not local militia. The two spies move south of the Big Timber Creek, attempting to approach the fort and glean further intelligence. Unable to reach the fort quickly, and deterred by its scout patrols, the two men sleep off a trail northeast of Woodbury. The following day, Jacob and Mahlon decide a direct approach will raise less suspicion. The men visit the Whitall house, looking to purchase food, and tell Ann Whitall they are traveling to Greenwich on the Cohansey River. Ann, who has refused to leave her beautiful home and garden to the ravages of war, asks if they are sailors. Mahlon answers, "Looking for work Ma'am."

Although the Whitall home is less than four hundred yards south of the fort, near the beach, Ann has not allowed the home to be used as barracks. She explains that many of the soldiers have visited the house for medicines or food, as her garden is full of medicinal herbs and vegetables. Ann tells Mahlon men in the fort are sailors from Providence or Newport and many are African or Narragansett Indians. Ann mentions, "A black man and woman earlier broke bread at this table." The man is a sailor as well, "But no regular soldier as the other men in the fort," explains Ann. Jacob grabs Mahlon's arm, telling Ann Whitall the man sounds like a friend. Ann's good nature is free of suspicion, and she tells them Moriah indicated the two were headed for Woodbury. Jacob does not let go of Mahlon's arm and replies, "After we purchase food, we may try and catch up with them," and Ann shows no suspicion for Woodbury is on the way to the Cohansey River. Minutes latter, the two men are headed to their horses and quickly on the south road back to Woodbury.

Colonel von Donop will appreciate the knowledge that tested regular troops, not militia, are manning the palisade walls of Fort Mercer. The

Hessian forces are already on the move and Jacob plans to capture Ephraim, delivering him to the count while the Hessian army camps near Haddonfield. Mahlon and Jacob catch up with the duo in the pines outside Woodbury. Jacob believes the two spies will wait out any fighting in the town, and he resigns to apprehend them before they may enter. He sends Mahlon to flank them to the south, setting up at the edge of the woods. Jacob plans to shoot the horse from under Ephraim and Mahlon is to take down the woman's mount following his shot. Moriah will be used as leverage to gain Ephraim's compliant surrender. Before Moriah and Ephraim can exit the woods, Jacob is in position and signals Mahlon. Jacob steadies his rifle against a tree limb and pulls the trigger. Ephraim's horse is hit in the chest, rearing violently before coming to ground. Moriah's horse is startled, and she wheels abruptly, causing Mahlon's shot to miss wide. Ephraim shouts for Moriah to escape back to the fort. She hesitates, shooting her pistol toward Mahlon.

Ephraim tells her pointedly, "It is the Doan, you must warn Greene and bring back help if you can." He continues, "Quickly, before they may reload!" Moriah glares at Ephraim and then spurs her horse back toward the fort. Ephraim has gambled well. Mahlon stands, aiming his pistol at Moriah, while Ephraim spins up his rifle from a shoulder, carefully aims, and shoots Mahlon above the knee at sixty paces. Jacob, still reloading his rifle, calls out for Mahlon whom he knows has been hit. Mahlon is alive but shouts that his leg is broken and bleeding badly. Ephraim is quickly reloading his rifle and will have it and a second pistol ready to fire in under a minute. Meanwhile, Jacob encroaches ever closer, and Ephraim is forced to sends him to ground with a pistol shot. As Jacob pleads with Mahlon to keep his head low, Ephraim offers a deal. Ephraim tells Jacob to throw out his rifle, keep his pistol, and allow Ephraim to move around to his horse. Jacob may freely tend Mahlon's wounds upon Ephraim's departure. Jacob replies in the Algonquin tongue, and Ephraim has an answer without knowing the words. Stalemate ensues.

Mahlon reveals his pain, causing Ephraim to employ a second approach. He explains to Jacob, "Your people have no future with the likes of Count von Donop. Soldiers in the fort, Narragansett, Mohegan and Algonquin brothers are American soldiers fighting tyranny. They understand that men like the count will continue to take from white and nonwhite alike." Ephraim tells Jacob, "I've been to Europe where destitute men live in the millions, serving men like the count. The poor in Europe are numerous as stars, and like locust will poor across America's shores so men like von Donop have access to cheap labor and fodder for wars." He continues, "New immigrants will devour new lands sold at a profit by the count and leave nothing for your people." Deep in thought, Jacob has not moved for quarter an hour, but finally cannot take the pleadings of young Mahlon and throws out his rifle toward Ephraim. Jacob simply yells, "Go!"

Jacob wraps Mahlon's wound tightly. Ephraim has left with his horse, while Jacob prepares his young "brother" for travel back to the Whitall home. Jacob has little choice, Mahlon is his priority, and he follows Ephraim back toward Fort Mercer. Jacob knows Ann Whitall possesses the medicine and supplies needed to treat Mahlon, and there may be a skilled surgeon attached to Colonel Greene's command.

Ephraim is in sight of the Whitall farm when Moriah and three colonial riders meet him on the road. Moriah is spoiling for a fight and is pained to relinquish the chase. He convinces her to let it go as he has made a pact with the Doan. The man is a Lenape brave, not Moses or Abraham. The second man, almost a boy, is the young Mahlon Doan.

A colonial officer takes leave to ride back to the fort and report to Colonel Greene that he may expect an assault by Colonel von Donop. The regimental officer orders the two remaining soldiers to stay with Moriah. One man is a Narragansett Indian from Providence and the other, a sergeant, is a clearly prosperous African man. Ephraim believes Mahlon will be brought back to the Whitall farm, as he is seriously wounded, and that the Lenape brave may be persuaded to abandon his loyalties to Colonel von Donop. Regardless, the sergeant indicates he will arrest the men if they do return to Fort Mercer, while Moriah has plans of her own for the two men's immediate future. She has never taken kindly to becoming the target of such men.

Freedom's Promise

Battle of Red Bank • Fort Mercer, New Jersey • October 22, 1777

A bandaged, but whole, Mahlon Doan lies unconscious on a dining table in the Whitall home. Ann Whitall convinced Moriah, who wanted to smother the young man, to instead save his life. Ann pressed upon Moriah the importance of God's plan, and that she should save a life if she is able. "A young man may repent his trespass," states Ann, who also tells Moriah, "You may know God's grace by forgiving a man."

Colonel Greene has refused all aid for the two spies but dares not execute the Lenape brave while many Algonquin serve under him. Greene leaves the two spies in Ephraim's custody, and Jacob is imprisoned, under constant guard, in a small outer building near the Whitall home. He will not escape, and the Hessians will sorely miss his knowledge. Before nine in the morning on Wednesday a teenaged runner, Jonas Cattell, arrives from Haddonfield. Jonas alerts Colonel Greene that thousands of Hessian soldiers approach the fort. Ephraim is left with a dilemma. Mahlon Doan cannot yet be moved, and Moriah chooses to stay with Ann. Jacob can identify Moriah, and Ephraim is not willing to risk his escape. His instinct prods him and he neither wants to leave Moriah, who will not be dissuaded, nor abandon the coming fight to be fought by patriot soldiers who once were slaves. Ephraim determines to offer Jacob a bargain.

Ann Whitall earlier informs Jacob of Ephraim's intercession with Colonel Greene to spare his life. Jacob expects Ephraim to require a confession and intelligence on Tory networks in the region. He is surprised when Ephraim explains that his handlers require no additional information on the Doan's activities. Ephraim will give Jacob his liberty, but only if he makes a sacred pact, on Mahlon's life, to end his support of the Doan. Moreover, he will need to enter Fort Mercer with Ephraim and help fight the Hessian soldiers if need be. Jacob agrees. The decision is not difficult. Captured spies face near certain death, and he knows his service will provide Mahlon the best chance for survival under Moriah's care.

Count von Donop leads a powerful Hessian attack force. Three heavy regiments of grenadier assault troops, as well as a light infantry regiment, and battalions of *jäger* riflemen and mounted scouts are on the march. The Hessians also tow a dozen mobile field cannon and howitzers down to Fort Mercer. Leaving Haddonfield hours past midnight, they are stymied at Clements Bridge over the Timber Creek. The bridge has been withdrawn and this nearly doubles the distance the Hessians must march. Instead of arriving before nine in the morning, their forward units arrive at Fort Mercer after noon. Expecting a fort manned by militia, Colonel von Donop assumes his overwhelming force will frighten the rebels into immediate submission. The count's entire plan is distorted by a lack of intelligence, an intelligence Jacob can't provide, and this blindness allows Carl von Donop to default to his weakness, his arrogance.

Colonel Greene confronts Ephraim, who enters the fort with Jacob prior to midday. Jacob's in irons, however, Greene is adamant that he cannot spare manpower to guard the spy. Ephraim explains the man is turned, but Colonel Greene will have none of it, exclaiming that if Ephraim wants custody of the man their legs must be chained, insuring Jacob will fight for his life. Additionally, they will be posted in the most exposed landward parapet with a few sharpshooters. Jacob dares not smile, as he knows Ephraim is cornered by his own plan. Before the smith finishes locking the two men into ankle irons, with a five-foot connecting chain, shouts can be heard, and Ephraim knows the German's have arrived.

Once in the parapet tower, Jacob and Ephraim are pushed into the outer corner, so they are least in the way. Jacob states, "We may die with a view," and a Black man of the 1st Rhode Island gives him a glare and says to Ephraim, "If this man can't hole a button at fifty paces, I'll shoot him myself." Jacob is not armed with a pear knife and will reload for Ephraim, but soldiers know guns become available in dead men's hands. Ephraim's weapon is special, a custom 45-caliber rifle made in Lancaster. His rifle is not a hunting tool. Rather, it is a carbine with a much shorter barrel, designed for high accuracy within a hundred paces. Ephraim has never hunted deer, only men, and his rifle is fit for purpose. A Hessian drummer is thumping a beat and a group of officers, one a British major, approach the fort. Colonel Greene sends out a subordinate for the parlay, and Jacob cannot see the count. The

British officer is an interpreter for the German's, sent by Colonel von Donop to accept the fort's surrender. The negotiation does not proceed as planned, yet the Englishman presumes to yell out loudly for the fort's defenders to lay down their rebellious arms and, "Declare fealty to his majesty, King George." A loud, "Nooo!" is the resounding response from the defenders and the major responds with loud threats, warning no quarter will be given to those who resist an assault. The British officer is further confounded when the patriots respond for him to "hide" his threats. Ephraim turns to Jacob with a smile, and says, "At least you'll be spared the noose." Both men know an attack is now inevitable.

Colonel von Donop is visiting the Whitall home when he hears the loud remonstrations from the fort's defenders. He sighs slightly to himself but is resigned to his duty. The die is cast, and he has but one course of action. The colonel bids his accompanying artillery officers rejoin their batteries in the eastern woods. He then instructs his adjutant to have the regiments prepare bundled branches. The bundles will help fill the trenches at the base of the fort's mud walls. An artillery barrage will commence within the hour.

The count's thoughts turn toward his preparations, as his men have not brought ladders or hooks, not even axes to breach the fort's defenses. Since defeat is not an option, Carl von Donop must show his men courage. Sure of surrender, his army has brought no wagons to evacuate the wounded and there will now be great need. Colonel von Donop inspects Mahlon Doan, who is alive but in an unconscious state. The count inquires as to Jacob's whereabouts. Ann Whitall explains that Mahlon was captured with a Lenape brave who may remain alive inside the fort. She explains that her "servant," Moriah, is a skilled healer and the count acknowledges the curious woman. The count now has more reason to capture the fort, as he cannot afford Jacob's knowledge to spread.

The sun dips low in the western horizon, beyond the Delaware River, and Hessian cannon ring out in unison without warning. Three-pound explosive iron balls blast overhead or ricochet off the tops of the palisade walls at speeds near two hundred miles per hour. As Jacob and Ephraim duck, a Black soldier behind has his head torn from its body. The man is quickly removed from the parapet. The blood will cause the marksmen to lose footing, but Jacob has already acquired a rifle from the body. Light Hessian infantry are running toward the fort, in perpendicular columns, carrying bales of branches to fill the trenches at the base of the walls. Waves of grenadier assault troops are marching fast behind and attacking all three landward sides of the fort simultaneously.

More than a thousand men charge toward the fort. Ignoring the light infantry, Jacob takes aim at a Hessian officer leading his grenadier, and he drops the man at two hundred paces with a shot through the waist. Colonel Greene earlier instructs his men to aim just above the wide hip belts worn by the Hessian soldiers, and his men are excellent marksmen.

Once the light infantry starts laying bales at the base of the walls, the Hessian cannonade ceases. The threat now, thinks Jacob, is the jäger sharpshooters targeting defenders from the safety of the woods. The wiz of rifled shots, from the tree line, passes their heads and Jacob joins Ephraim in targeting grenadier as they approach the base of the wall. Reaching the trenches, the assault troops are more difficult to target, but Ephraim calls out, "They have no ladders or axes in hand." The defenders are amazed. Hessian attackers cannot breach the wall and resort to climbing on shoulders to attempt pulling each other up and over the palisades. The assault troopers, with their heavy ensemble, are easy targets for the determined defenders. Few Hessians make it to the parapets, as most are shot, left cowering under cover of the trench or flee defeated for the woods. The fleeing troops leave many of their wounded brethren bleeding in the field.

Ephraim, on Jacob's left, cry's out. A strange sound for a hard man, thinks Jacob, but he immediately sees Ephraim has been hit. A *jäger's* ball nicks his skull, and he is on his knees trying to stop the bleeding from a concussed head. Either in self-preservation or in natural state of solidarity, Jacob tears part of his shirt to try and bandage Ephraim's head. Ephraim waves him off and hands up his rifle to Jacob, yelling coldly, "The Count, the count is below to your left, quickly!" Jacob spots von Donop and a second officer trying to direct their men within the trench. Count von Donop is not shielding his person in cowardice thinks Jacob, but as he takes aim with Ephraim's rife, marveling at its lightness, he remembers the pressure of the count's condescending hand on his shoulder. Jacob aims low for center mass and begins applying pressure to the trigger. Thinking of Moses' future, in the instant, he shoots Colonel von Donop through the right thigh instead. The count's body jerks with the sharp pain and falls on top of his adjutant, who is already dead. Count von Donop moves himself closer to the safety of the wall, and he immediately thinks it would be better had he been killed outright. Many of his troopers bravely continue the assault, but the count knows the battle is lost.

Jacob meant to wound the count, and he is not sure if the change in target caused the bullet to enter too close to the man's groin. If the femoral artery is cut, Jacob knows the count will be dead shortly. Nevertheless, it is a serious wound and the German's cause is lost. As the sun begins to set, casting shadow over the fields, the Hessians are in full retreat. Many soldiers cling below the palisade walls, hoping to be captured and not killed. The groans of the wounded and dying is bittersweet reminder, for the defenders, of the fate that may have been theirs were it not for God's hand and the Hessian's lack of foresight.

The battle is won, and celebration commences in the fort. A few unlucky Rhode Island soldiers climb out on the palisade wall, waving off the German's, and are shot dead by *jäger* marksmen covering the retreat from the edge of the woods. Ephraim pulls at Jacob's leg and bids him not lose his head. He unties the flag, previously given him by Moriah, and used to stem his bleeding head wound. Ephraim hands up the flag to Jacob, bidding him tie the colors to his rifle.

Carl von Donop is conscious, though he wishes he were not, and he forces his retreating soldiers to leave his broken body on the field for the enemy. The sky is a beautiful indigo blue, with a red orange hue, as faint glimmers of white light recede with the sun. He rests his head deep in the grass, sighs for what is lost and dreams of the stars above. Carl hopes he will be with them soon, yet a flutter of color peaks his attention back to earth. Lifting his head briefly, he views a unique standard. Not the union flag, but a flag of stars in constellation. Betsy has sewn the flag especially for her guardian, Ephraim, and bid Moriah present the gift. Within the center field of red stripe, Betsy has embroidered in a bold golden stitch …

FREEDOM'S PROMISE

ACKNOWLEDGEMENTS AND NOTES

German translation and associated editing are courtesy of Eva R. Priestley, USA.

Art illustration remaining under artist copyright, courtesy of Mark Maritato.

High resolution photographs courtesy of the author.

Thanks to the revolutionarywarjournal.com, durhamhistoricalsociety. org, wikipedia.org, the Washington Crossing State Historic Park Museum in Hopewell, NJ, the Red Bank Battlefield Historical Park & Museum, 100 Hessian Ave., National Park, NJ, the New Hope Historical Society, newhopehs.org, the Pennsylvania Historical & Museum Commission Historical Marker Program, Harrisburg, PA, The Metropolitan Museum of Art, 1000 Fifth Ave. at 82nd Street, New York, NY, the Mercer Museum, 84 South Pine Street, Doylestown, PA, the Brandywine River Museum of Art, 1 Hoffman's Mill Road, Chadds Ford, PA, The Free Library of Philadelphia, 1901 Vine Street, Philadelphia, PA, the Joseph P. Tustin Papers Archive at the Harvey A. Andruss Library, Bloomsburg University of Pennsylvania, 400 East 2nd Street, Bloomsburg, PA.

Fig. 1, Page i and 71

Pyle, Howard. *The Nation Makers*, 1903, Brandywine River Museum of Art, Chadds Ford, PA, collections.brandywine.org

Pyle's depiction of colonial forces in action at the Battle of Brandywine is iconic. The painting is not a commissioned piece, but a representation clearly dear to his heart. Howard Pyle's school in Chadds Ford, Pennsylvania, is very near the battlefield. His painting captures the determination and youthfulness of the American Continental Army attempting to defend their capital, Philadelphia. Young men who desire the freedom to pursue the opportunities previously afforded their fathers and grandfathers. As in the depiction, many of the leaders and founders of the revolution, with notable exceptions, were middle-aged men who had already tasted opportunity in the new world.

The Revolutionary War, at its essence, is a struggle for control of land resources. Britain meant to control and contain the spread of the colonists beyond the Appalachian Mountains, Ohio River Valley and the Iroquois Six-Nations. The colonial population grew three quarters of a thousand percent in the preceding seventy-six years, reaching nearly two and a half million. A great portion of the southern population lived as slaves, but north of Delaware there are few, and the free population in the north is well over a million at the outbreak of war. Demographics were highly skewed toward the young, as many colonists had been highly fertile. The result was a population born in America, filled with distain for royal power, and seeking opportunities in cities and on the frontier. Britain looked to control or deny this opportunity. For George Washington, whose dear departed older brother helped found the Ohio Land Company, the war would help settle whether the land speculators of the coming quarter century lived in Philadelphia, New York and Virginia rather than London or Frankfurt. Hundreds of thousands of young Americans simply wanted a shot at opportunity, and they knew they needed to defeat the British first.

Fig. 2, Page 13

McFadden, Patrick Michael. *The Walking Bridge*, Nov. 2006, author's permission

The pedestrian bridge spanning the Delaware River resides at the location of the Tory's ferry and the Temple Bar. Current bridge built upon the remains of structures from the previous centuries. Bull's Island resides on the left bank, while the famous Black Bass Inn and Restaurant, the Temple Bar, resides on the right, within the historic hamlet of Lumberville, Pennsylvania. The Doan gang used the Tory's ferry frequently, as the family land is only a handful of miles up the Paunacussing Creek and to the northwest on a rolling plateau of farmland partially defined by the steep shale cliffs above the creek.

Fig. 3, Pages 15 & 97

Map of the provinces of New York and New Jersey, with a part of Pennsylvania and Quebec. 1777, Lotter Albrecht, Library of Congress: loc.gov The original map is large and highly detailed, depicting the northern British colonial possessions from northern Quebec to Baltimore, in the south, from the Atlantic seaboard as far east as Nova Scotia to the western frontier in Pennsylvania and the nations of the Iroquois confederation in western New York state. The raw TIFF file can be viewed at loc.gov. A second map may also be instructive: An accurate plan of the country between New York and Philadelphia, with the disposition of forces. 1777, Pyle Stephen, Library of Congress: loc.gov. This secondary map details the disposition and movement of forces prior to the Battle of Trenton and may be viewed on pages 98 and 99.

The modern river town of New Hope, Pennsylvania, is marked as Well's Ferry on Lotter's 1777 map. The town lies less than six miles south of the Tory's ferry and the Temple Bar, while the well know modern shopping destination of Peddler's Village on the Old York Road, near the former Indian village of Aquetong, is a few miles as the crow flies to Temple Bar. The map maker was unaware Well's Ferry was sold or perhaps had an English client, as Coryell's Ferry is the correct name by 1776. The ferry operator denied Lord Cornwallis passage as English forces chased Washington into Bucks County in mid December 1776. English officers lit the ferry's lamp, on the Jersey banks, one evening in a call for service that is never answered.

Fig. 4, Pages 19 & 100

Pyle, Howard. *Battle of Bunker Hill*, 1897, Location unknown, presumed stolen

Scene depicts the second attack upon Breed's Hill by the 52nd regiment of foot, with a grenadier company in the foreground. Research indicates that the British may not have advanced in such close ranks nor overburdened with heavy campaign packs, however, the British Admiralty was uncooperative when Pyle requested details for his work. The piece written for allthingsliberty.com by Don N. Hagist is highly informative. Titled: *Dissecting the Battle of Bunker Hill Painting* by Howard Pyle, Sep. 26, 2013. The FBI lists the famous painting as stolen art, as it went missing in 2001.

Fig. 5, Page 27

De Steuben, Charles. *Frederick William II of Hesse-Kassel*, 1843, Palace Museum in Pavlousk, St. Petersburg, Russian Federation

Noble Count of Hesse-Kassel, painted in formal military style of late 18th – early 19th century. Frederick had strong familial links with Britain,

Norway, Denmark and Russia. He married for love, a daughter of Czar Nicholas I, nicknamed Adini, who tragically died the same year. The connection between the ruling families of Britain, Hesse and Russia is certainly ironic given our story. Anyone born in the twenty-first century may not imagine a world in which North America is a fragmented continent, but our unity is hard won and fully planned by our founders. Humanity may not have survived the twentieth century were it not for this great unity.

We can only hope that future leaders and citizens heed the critical message in the *Judgment of Solomon*, a message prophetic for his biblical homeland. Yet the savior of our story is African and an American by choice. Ephraim's continent of birth offers a heartbreaking lesson in unity. The vast continent is mysterious, filled with beauty and diversity. Many of her people harbor enormous talent and possess a wealth of human kindness and empathy. Nonetheless, political disunity within and without national borders prevents Africa from reaching her full potential. Americans of all backgrounds should cherish what we have, as imperfect as it may be. Our unity is our shield and provides a capacity for change that lesser nations, on all continents, lack. Such a precious thing, won and kept so dearly, should not be lightly discarded in the bonfires of intolerance, ignorance and bigotry.

Art and art history can often inform us to the sensibilities of previous generations. Charles de Steuben was a noted painter within the royal courts of Europe during the nineteenth century, more so as he was a member of the nobility himself. De Steuben was the son of the Duke of *Württemberg*, and he lived for a short while in St. Petersburg as his father served in the Czar's army. The young Charles studied drawing at the Art Academy in the city and became close with members of the Czar's family. De Steuben's painting, *Battle of Poitiers*, depicting Charles Martel and the Franks defeating an Arab and Berber army invading France from Spain and North Africa in 732 AD is itself iconic. The painting hangs in the Palace of Versailles and should inform European leaders today as to the knowledge of their leaders at the time De Steuben was painting. Charles de Steuben and the rulers of Europe's golden age understood that a thousand years of history could be decided on a battlefield in a single day or even an hour. Americans should heed this knowledge since technology makes the whole world a battlefield, and it will take far less than an hour to destroy what thousands of years has built.

Fig. 6, Page 29

Maritato, Mark. *The Battle of Brooklyn*, 2015, Artist's studio, maritato. com, artist's permission

Lord Stirling and the men of Maryland stand tall in the face of the enemy. A remnant of the 1st Maryland regiment holds off advancing brigades of Scottish highlanders and Hessian grenadier lead by the Count Carl von Donop and Lord Cornwallis. The Stone House still stands as a park and museum in Brooklyn, New York. The park is located near the Gowanus Canal. Backed up against the Gowanus, the entire remaining Maryland unit, as depicted by Mark, gave their lives willingly so our revolution could live on.

Fig. 7, Page 34

Chambers, Thomas. *The Constitution and The Guerriére*, 1845, Metropolitan Museum of Art, New York City, metmuseum.org

The USS Constitution and her sister ships serve the young nation well prior to the outbreak of war with Great Britain in 1812, earlier helping force the pirates of the Barbary States in North Africa into a submissive treaty. The new American frigates heavily disrupt British merchant shipping at the outbreak of war in 1812, and the Royal Navy quickly sails into action. The Admiralty in London is set to be shocked. As the painting by Chambers illustrates, American heavy frigates, such as the USS Constitution, come to dominate British frigates in "man to man" duels on the high seas. The losses are a direct afront to the British air of superiority, as British warships accustomed to victory become the Hector to the new American Achilles.

HMS Guerriére is dispatched, with a squadron of ships, early in the war to attempt capture or destruction of the USS Constitution. Tracking her northeast of Boston the British were unable to intercept, however, and Guerriére separates from her group to refit in Halifax, Nova Scotia. British captains are a very proud lot, and Guerriére's commander likely thought he ruled the waves when the Constitution appears on the horizon deep in the Atlantic Ocean off the great George's Banks. The British warship had become the hunted and yet gave battle eagerly. Seasoned English sailors are dismayed as their cannon balls seem to bounce off the heavy American oak paneling of the USS Constitution's hull. During the battle an American sailor shouts out, "Huzzah, her sides are made of Iron," and a legend is born.

The USS Constitution, "Old Ironsides," fully de-masts Guerriére and turns her into a sinking hulk. The captain of the USS Constitution commends his English adversary on his fighting spirit and allows the man, Captain Dacres, to retain his sword and his mother's bible.

We should note how large these ships are. Constitution enters the fight with 480 sailors and Marine infantry aboard. Guerriére has a compliment of 272 sailors and Royal Marine infantry. Most ironic, ten of Guerriére's sailors are impressed Americans, highlighting a cause of the war. Captain Dacres was prescient in not forcing these men to fight that day, and the Constitution's Captain Hull takes the remaining British crew back to Boston in triumph. Beyond the loss of a battlecruiser, English casualties are 93 versus 14 on the American side.

Unfortunate for the British, the victory is no fluke or whim of fate. Having sailed from Boston to Cape Verde, near Africa, USS Constitution and the smaller sloop-of-war, USS Hornet, arrive off the coast of Brazil in December 1812. The American ships catch an unlucky HMS Bonne Citoyenne, a sloop-of-war on post duty, fitting repairs in Salvador harbor. The British vessel is England bound from Rio de Janeiro with half a million pounds Stirling in silver coin when forced into port. As a neutral Portuguese city, the Americans could not attack, and the British Captain, Greene, dares not leave port with such a bounty on board. James Lawrence, the commander of the Hornet, sends Greene a challenge to meet ship to ship on the high seas, but Greene passes on the offer not believing that USS Constitution will allow his ship to sail free if she emerges victorious from the duel. Constitution, now under Commodore Bainbridge's command, leaves Hornet and heads back out to sea looking for additional prey.

The morning of December 29 she spots a target sailing west over the horizon. HMS Java, a 40-gun frigate, is sailing for Bombay, India, and looking to stop over in Brazil. She left Portsmouth, England, in November with a full, yet somewhat green, compliment. Moreover, Captain Henry Lambert is not the only senior British commander or official on board. Java carries near 500 souls, as the newly appointed Governor of Bombay, Lt. General Sir Thomas Hislop, and his staff, are on board. Additionally, the new crew for the HMS Cornwallis, under construction in India, is also on ship, as is a second British captain in transit.

Any boarding will be bloody given the large compliment on USS Constitution, as the equivalent of two regiments would fight hand-to-hand in a confined space. The British will not be afforded such opportunity, as Constitution's tactics and broadsides are too much for the slightly lighter British frigate. The Americans feign to flee, likely trying to lure the enemy out of popular sea-lanes, and Java unwisely gives chase. The following day the two vessels engage in running broadsides and come close enough to become entangled with the other's rigging. Constitution has her bridge shot away and Bainbridge is wounded. Eventually, Java's masts collapse, and Captain Lambert is mortally wounded by an American sharpshooter. With her masts and rigging dragging to a side, Java can only fire from one side, and she is forced to surrender when a repaired Constitution comes in for the kill. Again, Constitution has so badly mauled a British vessel that she cannot be taken as a battle prize and is sunk on New Years day. Java suffers 124 casualties, with Lambert killed, while Constitution suffers 66 casualties.

Although wounded during the engagement, Commodore Bainbridge proves that USS Constitution is a fighting match for the British no matter her captain. Bainbridge is saddened to hear of Lambert's death as the British officer put up a valiant fight. The realities of war may have prevented a personal rejoicing, however, a copper plaque for the yet completed HMS Cornwallis is recovered from HMS Java. Surely, the commodore enjoys some ironic pleasure from the thought of recovering the namesake of the man who surrendered to George Washington at the battle of Yorktown, as it was Washington who chose the name for the USS Constitution.

A more subtle irony lies in HMS Java's name. Being named for the primary tea-producing island of the Indonesian archipelago is certainly ironic, given that taxes on imported tea from the Orient partially sparked the Revolutionary War. The British East India Company spends so much royal silver purchasing Chinese tea leaves that they need the Chinese hooked on opium, attempting to recoup their silver and equalize the firm's and thereby the British Empire's current account. The war this trade sparks with China, in the early nineteenth century, provides vindication for America's desire to free itself from such avarice. Clearly, the American Revolutionary War is justified, and yet even today we need to be on constant guard for such usurious schemes.

Fig. 8, Page 39

Currier & Ives: *The Heroine on Monmouth.* 1876, Library of Congress: loc.gov

The depiction of a woman manning an artillery piece during battle is well known. The image of a "Molly Pitcher" during the Battle of Monmouth in 1778 gives life to a legend that was often real. The piece written for teachtnhistory.org is instructive, and titled: *Margaret Corbin: Molly Pitcher?* Accredited source: Carol Berkin, *Revolutionary Women: Women in the Struggle for America's Independence* (New York, 2006), xi, 138–9. The theory discussed is that Molly Pitcher is a common colloquialism, used by patriot soldiers and their descendants to describe the numerous women who assisted artillery crews in battle during the Revolutionary War. The name itself, Molly Pitcher, is proof of the theory. As depicted in the lithographic image, an empty pail of water lies on the ground at the feet of the heroine as she operates the rammer on the cannon in place of the dead crewman lying below her. The work by Melissa Lukeman Bohrer, *Glory, Passion, and Principle*, 2003, 159–162, also discusses "eight remarkable women at the core of the American Revolution," including the two leading contenders for the inspiration of the colloquialism, Margaret Cochran Corbin and Mary Hays McCauley. Mary actually fought alongside the men at the Battle of Monmouth, and both Mary and Margaret were from the Cumberland County, Pennsylvania, region and had husbands likely attached to artillery units formed under Thomas Proctor.

The lithographic image would have been far to real for Margaret Cochran Corbin, whose young husband John died manning a cannon at the Battle of Fort Washington, Upper Manhattan, during the fall of 1776. Margaret, like many women during the war, traveled with her husband who served in Washington's army. Rapidly fired during battle, the cannons required cleaning and dousing with water to prevent them fouling and overheating. There is no doubt that countless women worked with the artillery crews, ferrying heavy pails of water between a source and the cannons. These women operated under fire and shared the same risks as the men. In the face of the enemy, clearly, many of these women stood a post and manned a gun when their men were disabled or killed in action. Margaret Corbin is a famous example of this heroism, and she very well may be the first known case of a woman replacing her slain husband in such a manner during the early war.

Margaret is nearly forgotten, replaced with a fading colloquialism, yet she was not widely honored by her own neighbors during her lifetime either. Margaret was barely thirty when the long Revolutionary War ended, and she was left without a husband, fair countenance or the use of her left arm. Margaret was grievously wounded by Hessian cannon fire as Colonel Johann Rahl's troops successfully stormed her position outside the walls of Fort Washington. The Congress did not forget her gallantry in battle nor the service her patriotism provided by helping to inspire a nation. For her actions and injuries suffered in one short battle, the Congress provided her the partial pension of a Continental soldier for her remaining years.

Fig. 9, Page 55

Maritato, Mark. *42nd Foot vs. Cilley's Picked Men*, 2010, Private owner, maritato.com, artist's permission

Terrific representation of a royal highland regiment engaged with regular Continental soldiers. A similar scene would have taken place north of Mount Holly, New Jersey, as highlanders of the famed Black Watch brigade, the 42nd, engaged with troops under Colonel Griffin's Philadelphia / South Jersey regiment prior to the Battle of Trenton.

We are confident Colonel Thomas Stirling led the highlanders. Research performed by Tim Abbott, who blogs under greensleeves.typepad.com indicates that Stirling arrived with Howe's army and participated in the Battle of Long Island. According to this research, Stirling was easily one of the most experienced tactical commanders attached with the royal armies in North America, and personally oversaw the training of the highland battalions, preparing his men to fight in the open formation more suited to the features of America and utilized by the colonials and natives alike. Stirling was half way through a more than fifty-year military career with his prince's army. He must have had notoriety with his superior commanders as he was a member of the Scottish nobility, yet a second son, and famous for navigating the Ohio and Mississippi Rivers following the French and Indian War.

Following Pontiac's Rebellion, in which more than a dozen separate Indian tribes including Jacob's previously displaced Lenni-Lenape joined forces to attempt pushing the British settlers east of the Great Lakes and east toward the Appalachians, then Captain Stirling led a 100 man detachment of the 42nd down the Ohio River and receives control of Fort de Chartres on the Mississippi River south of St. Louis, Missouri. Stirling and his men winter at the fort and sail down to New Orleans in 1765, traveling to Pensacola, Florida, and then catching ship back for New York. Once in the city, they march for Philadelphia to rejoin their regiment.

The trip is quite the odyssey, and we can only wonder as to the relationship such a soldier would have had with Count von Donop. Thomas Stirling and the Black Watch serve with distinction during the remainder of the Revolutionary War and are often attached to Hessian leaders. By the end of the war, Thomas Stirling is promoted to Brigadier General and latter in life succeeds his brother as Sir Thomas Stirling, 5th Baronet Ardoch. Our research isn't clear as to Colonel Thomas Stirling's position when American Brigadier, William Alexander, "Lord Stirling" survives the martyrdom of the Maryland 1st regiment at the Battle of Brooklyn. However, William's strenuous desire to avoid capture by the highlanders is certainly understandable. Any soldier knowing William Alexander's claim on the Stirling title, a title coveted by the family of one of their senior officers, may have thought it propitious to dispatch the general rather than take the man prisoner.

Fig. 10, Page 58

Leutze, Emanuel. *Washington Crossing the Delaware*, 1851, Metropolitan Museum of Art, New York City, metmuseum.org

Fig. 11, Page 67

McFadden, Patrick Michael. *Freedom's Promise*, August 2020, author's permission

Fig. 12, Page 83

Rossetti, Dante Gabriel. *Kissing the Sword of Deliverance*, 1863, Strasbourg Museum of Modern and Contemporary Art, Strasbourg, France, en.musees.Strasbourg.eu/museum

The painting of Joan of Arc is a fitting allegory for our *Fidelia*. Joan lived during the early fifteenth century, in the waning period of the Hundred

Years' War, when the English had successfully reduced the French Kingdom and exerted sovereignty over a large portion of modern France. France was fractured and a shell of her former power. Isolation and desolation bore heavy on the French people who remained loyal to their king. Joan, an illiterate peasant, rose from obscurity, claiming a "calling" from the Archangel Michael and led the French people to freedom.

Joan lived in Domrémy, in the far northeast of France, near modern Luxembourg, then part of the Germanic Holy Roman Empire. Alsace-Lorraine, the border region near her home, was still being contested by great powers in the twentieth century. However, Joan's town remained loyal to France throughout the centuries. Maps from Joan's time, such as that delineating the Duchy of Bar, emphasize the disunity of fifteenth century France. Joan is martyred in her fight to reunite the French Kingdom, a unity that becomes critical for American Independence.

A large combined French and American army, that may have been more than half French, won the battle of Yorktown, the penultimate confrontation of the American Revolutionary War. The large blockading fleet that hemmed in the British on the Virginia coast during the battle is French as well. Unity provides France a great military, and unity allows her to push the Americans over the mantle of freedom.

Fig. 13, Page 95

McFadden, Patrick Michael. *Unknown Soldiers*, September 2020, author's permission

No fewer than twenty-three Continental Army soldiers are buried in the pictured field. While their patriot brethren march on Trenton, a dozen miles southeast of this field, soldiers who did not make the march due to sickness and exposure are buried near the Delaware River on Christmas Day 1776.

The soldiers are unknown, but one, Captain James Moore. Captain Moore, born in 1750, was an officer with the New York artillery regiment and a peer of Captain Alexander Hamilton. The captain died of camp fever, known today as a Typhus bacterial infection. Typhus and the Smallpox virus killed far more soldiers than did the royal army during the Revolutionary War. General Washington instituted an inoculation program in response.

He could not change the weather, however, and the colonies were in the midst of a "Little Ice Age," one of the coldest periods of the past thousand years in the Northern Hemisphere. Only two of Washington's men died assaulting Trenton, and their deaths were due to exposure. The Hessians, who suffered much greater casualties during the battle, had twenty-two men killed in action.

Freedom is Not Free

★ ★ ★ ★ ★ ★ ★ ★ ★ ★ ★

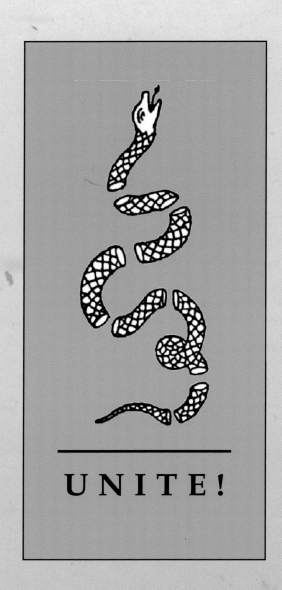

UNITE!

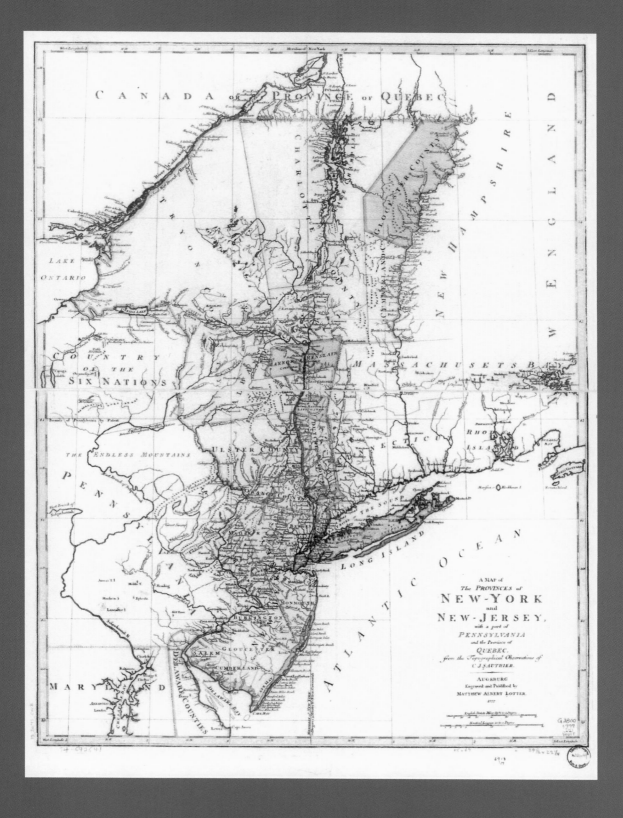

A MAP of
The PROVINCES of
NEW-YORK
and
NEW-JERSEY,
with a part of
PENNSYLVANIA
and the Province of
QUEBEC,
from the Topographical Observations of
C. J. SAUTHIER.

AUGSBURG
Engraved and Published by
MATTHEW ALBERT LOTTER.
1777

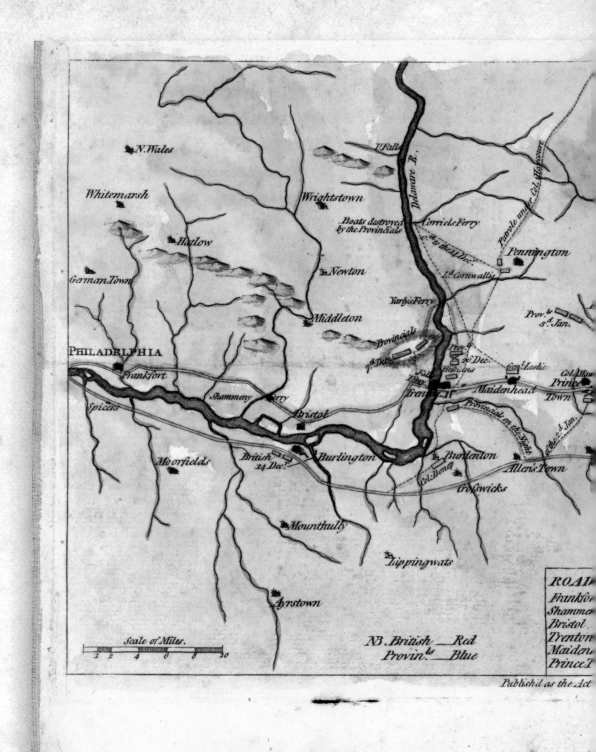

N.Wales

Whitemarsh

Hatlow

German Town

PHILADELPHIA

Frankfort

Spicers

Moorfields

Wrightstown

Newton

Middleton

Shammeny Ferry

Bristol

British 14 Dec.?

Burlington

Mounthilly

Ayrstown

V.Falls

Delaware R.

Boats destroyed by the Provincials

Corriels Ferry

Ld Cornwallis

Yarlys Ferry

Provincials 7th Dec:

Field Hessians

Trenton

Provincials 20 Dec:

Gen.l Leslie

Maidenhead

Provincials on the Whitt

Burlenton

Col. Donop

Allen's Town

Cobswicks

Parole under Col. Harcourt

Pennington

Prov.ls 3.d Jan.

Col.Maw

Prince Town

at the 2.d Jan.

Lippingwats

Scale of Miles.

1 2   4   6   8   10

NB. British ___ Red
Provin.ls ___ Blue

ROAD
Frankfor
Shammen
Bristol
Trenton
Maiden
Prince T

Publish'd as the Act

98   An American Tale of Freedom's Promise

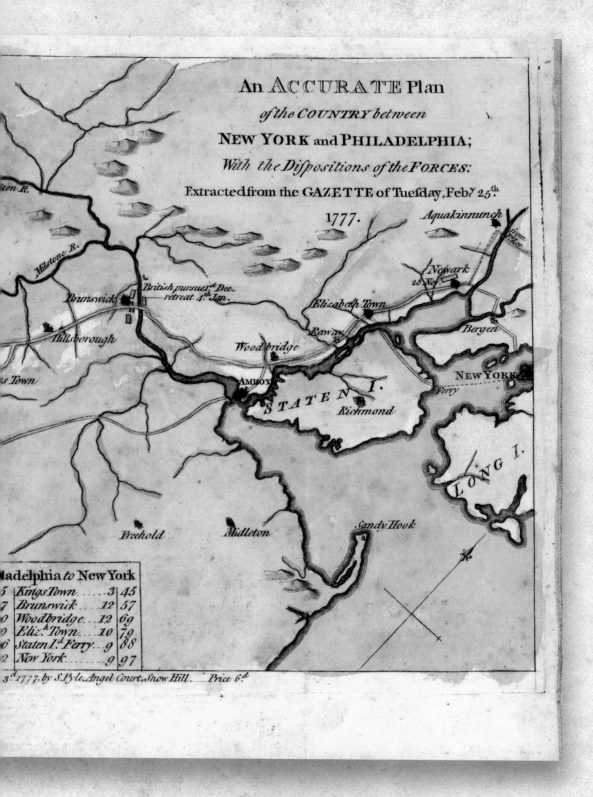

An ACCURATE Plan
of the COUNTRY between
NEW YORK and PHILADELPHIA;
With the Dispositions of the FORCES:
Extracted from the GAZETTE of Tuesday, Feb.y 25.th
1777.

adelphia *to* New York		
5	Kings Town........3	45
7	Brunswick......12	57
0	Woodbridge.....12	69
9	Eliz.h Town....10	79
6	Staten I.d Ferry..9	88
2	New York........9	97

3.d 1777. by S. Pyle, Angel Court, Snow Hill.   Price 6.d

The story is gripping and unique, splendidly illustrated, and imparts knowledge of the critical years of our nation's founding struggle, the American Revolution. The early war is the background, yet the true conflict is between a diverse set of spies, all Americans, whose loyalties are split between Britain and America.

Major battles of the war are largely confined to the Mid-Atlantic in 1776 & 1777, however, the war sparks in Boston during the spring of 1775. The die is cast in June at the Battle of Bunker Hill, the engagement depicted above in the iconic painting by Howard Pyle, as the bloody Pyrrhic victory damages the British Empire's pride. The king's honor will preclude a negotiated settlement agreeable to the Continental Congress in Philadelphia. The following summer, British General Howe, with his brother Admiral Lord Howe, returns to America with a massive invasion force. Royal forces include tens of thousands of Scottish soldiers and contracted German troops. As representatives of their king, the Howe brothers arrive as both military commanders and peace commissioners, with the power to process war or negotiate. The massive armada is a threat meant to preclude meaningful negotiation with the rebellious colonists, and new liberties for the thirteen colonies are not tabled. English peace means submission to the king's authority and a grant of pardon for the rebels. The Howe brothers offer no real concessions, simply a king's mercy. The people's representatives at Philadelphia choose to brave the consequences by signing The Declaration of Independence.

Libertas Americana coin medallion imaged by Heritage Auctions (HA.com).
Originally conceived by Benjamin Franklin in honor of the victory at Yorktown,
the 1782 design was furthered by Augustin Dupré and Esprit-Antoine Gibelin.

An early eighteenth century colonial Quaker homestead near Lahaska and Aquetong,
Pennsylvania. The author travels extensively in Bucks County and
central New Jersey, and he has a decades long interest in
the region's Revolutionary War history.

Printed in South Korea.